PRIMARY

WINDYKNOWE PRIMA

grammar
and
word study

- Parts of speech
- Understanding and choosing words
- Punctuation
- Figures of speech

verbs · plurals · confused words · full stops · apostrophes · conjunctions · similes · commas · determiners · homographs · synonyms · pronouns · prepositions · adjectives · adverbs · nouns · question marks

6246C

Primary grammar and word study *(Book G)*

Published by Prim-Ed Publishing 2010
Reprinted Prim-Ed Publishing 2014
Copyright© by R.I.C. Publications® 2008
ISBN 978-1-84654-211-4
PR–6246

Titles available in this series:

Primary grammar and word study *(Book A)*
Primary grammar and word study *(Book B)*
Primary grammar and word study *(Book C)*
Primary grammar and word study *(Book D)*
Primary grammar and word study *(Book E)*
Primary grammar and word study *(Book F)*
Primary grammar and word study *(Book G)*

Internet websites

In some cases, websites or specific URLs may be recommended. While these are checked and rechecked at the time of publication, the publisher has no control over any subsequent changes which may be made to webpages. It is *strongly* recommended that the class teacher checks *all* URLs before allowing pupils to access them.

View all pages online

Website: www.prim-ed.com

Primary grammar and word study – Book G

Foreword

Primary grammar and word study is a series of seven books designed to introduce pupils to parts of speech, ways to understand and choose words, punctuation and figures of speech.

Titles in this series:

- *Primary grammar and word study Book A* (Ages 5–6)
- *Primary grammar and word study Book B* (Ages 6–7)
- *Primary grammar and word study Book C* (Ages 7–8)
- *Primary grammar and word study Book D* (Ages 8–9)
- *Primary grammar and word study Book E* (Ages 9 –10)
- *Primary grammar and word study Book F* (Ages 10–11)
- *Primary grammar and word study Book G* (Ages 11–12)

Contents

Teachers notes

Learning about grammar and studying words helps pupils to better comprehend and use language when they are reading, writing, speaking, listening and viewing. Pupils can use the 'rules' or features of grammar to make their own writing and speaking understood by others and to understand the writing and speaking of others.

One major reference used during the writing of this series was the work of Professor George Stern who was a member of the Systemic Functional Grammar Association and PEN International.

Functional grammarians consider the way in which words are used within the context of a sentence; that is, they are more concerned with their FUNCTION in a particular context. In traditional grammar, the focus was more on defining the different parts of speech.

The book has been organised into four main sections covering a variety of aspects of grammar and word study:

- Parts of speech
- Understanding and choosing words
- Punctuation
- Figures of speech

Groups of two pages within each section follow a similar format.

Each pupil page is accompanied by a corresponding teachers page.

> Prim-Ed Publishing follows guidelines for punctuation and grammar as recommended by the *Style manual for authors, editors and printers*, sixth edition, 2002.
> Note, however, that teachers should use their preferred guidelines if there is a conflict.

Teachers notes pages

The **focus** of each corresponding pupil page is given.

A **definition** of each focus is given. For younger pupils, the definitions may be written in a more 'child-friendly' manner on the pupil page. For older pupils, the definition will be the same as that on the teachers page.

One or two **examples** of the focus are also given.

An **explanation** is given of the focus. This may also include the purpose for learning about the focus.

Any necessary information about how to use the worksheet with the pupils is also provided.

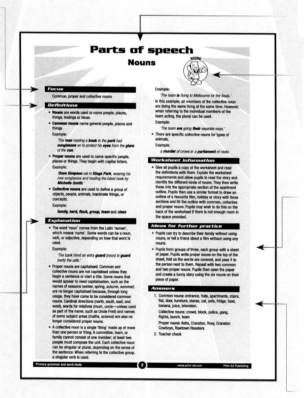

The **title** of each section is given.

A **literacy character** for each focus provides a visual representation and corresponds to the one on the pupil page.

Ideas for further practice to support or extend the pupil activity on the worksheet are supplied. Where possible, the activities will include other key learning areas or other areas of English, such as speaking and listening.

Answers are provided for pupil pages where necessary.

Teachers notes

Pupil activity pages

The **focus** of each pupil page is given. For younger pupils, the focus may be written in a more 'child-friendly' manner.

A **definition of the focus** is given which may be written in a more 'child-friendly' manner for younger pupils. For older pupils, the definition will be the same as that on the teachers page.

Clear, concise **instructions** for completing the pupil activities are supplied.

Activities on the pupil page require the pupils to **identify the focus** in context to see how and why it is used.

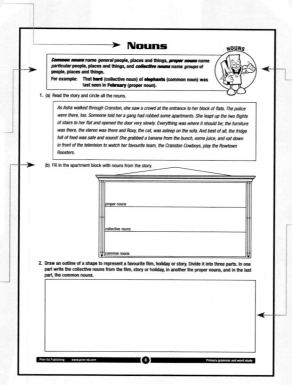

A **literacy character** for each focus provides a visual representation. Further information about the literacy characters can be found on pages vi and vii.

Interesting activities expect the pupils to **use and practise the focus** or to create examples of his/her own.

Note:

The pupil page activities give only a brief introduction to some of the concepts of grammar and word study included in this series of books. It is expected that teachers will use other resources and provide other activities to consolidate and extend pupils' understanding of these concepts and to introduce other age-appropriate grammar and word study concepts.

Teachers notes

Literacy characters appear on each pupil page throughout the series. The 'fun' characters provide a representation which is easily recognisable for visual-spatial learners and teachers to facilitate learning and teaching. Teachers may use the characters to select appropriate pupil pages throughout the different books in the series for individual pupil learning.

Parts of speech

NOUNS

VERBS

ADJECTIVES

ADVERBS

PRONOUNS

CONJUNCTIONS

DETERMINERS

PREPOSITIONS

Understanding and choosing words

HOMOGRAPHS

HOMOPHONES

WORD GROUPS

PLURALS

PREFIXES

SUFFIXES

SYNONYMS

ANTONYMS

WORD ORIGINS

Teachers notes

Literacy characters appear on each pupil page throughout the series. The 'fun' characters provide a representation which is easily recognisable for visual-spatial learners and teachers to facilitate learning and teaching. Teachers may use the characters to select appropriate pupil pages throughout the different books in the series for individual pupil learning.

Punctuation

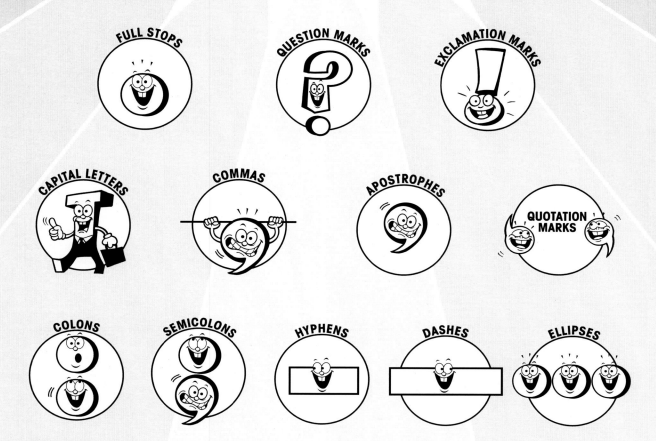

Figures of speech

Parts of speech checklist

Name of pupil	Nouns	Verbs	Adjectives	Adverbs	Pronouns	Conjunctions	Determiners	Prepositions

Understanding and choosing words checklist

Name of pupil	Homo-graphs	Homo-phones	Eponyms	Euphemisms	Plurals	Prefixes	Suffixes	Synonyms/ Antonyms	Word origins	Confused words

Punctuation checklist

Name of pupil	Full stops	Question marks	Exclamation marks	Capital letters	Commas	Apostrophes	Quotation marks	Colons/ Semicolons	Hyphens/ Dashes/ Ellipses

Figures of speech checklist

Name of pupil	Colloquialisms/Jargon	Hyperbole	Idioms	Similes/Metaphors	Proverbs

Curriculum links

Country	Subject	Level	Objectives
England	English	Year 6	• apply their growing knowledge of root words, prefixes and suffixes both to read aloud and to understand the meaning of new words they meet • continue to distinguish between homophones and other words which are often confused • how words are related by meaning as synonyms and antonyms • use further prefixes and suffixes and understand the guidelines for adding them • use expanded noun phrases to convey complicated information concisely • use adverbs to indicate degrees of possibility • use relative clauses beginning with *who, which, where, when, whose, that* or with an implied (i.e. omitted) relative pronoun • use commas to clarify meaning or avoid ambiguity in writing • use hyphens to avoid ambiguity • use semi-colons, colons or dashes to mark boundaries between main clauses • use colons to introduce a list
Northern Ireland	Language and Literacy	Key Stage 2	• use a variety of skills to spell words correctly • develop increasing competence in the use of grammar and punctuation to create clarity of meaning
Republic of Ireland	English Language	6th Class	• experience a growing elaboration and sophistication in the use of vocabulary and sentence structure • improve ability to recognise and understand words by using root words, prefixes and suffixes • express examples of jargon and slang • understand the functions and know the names of parts of speech; e.g. noun, verb, adjective, adverb, pronoun, conjunction, preposition and article • learn about and name the basic properties of nouns and verbs • become familiar with compound and complex sentences, and know and understand the terms 'phrase' and 'clause' • observe the conventions of grammar, punctuation and spelling in writing • use dictionaries and thesauruses to extend and develop vocabulary and spelling • discuss the value, truth or relevance of proverbs
Scotland	Literacy and English	Third	• explore word patterns • develop knowledge of punctuation and grammar • spell words and use spelling rules and specialist vocabulary • punctuate and structure different types of sentences with sufficient accuracy
Wales	English	Key Stage 3	• develop an understanding of the structure, vocabulary, grammar and punctuation of English • use the full range of punctuation in order to clarify meaning and create effect • use a wide range of vocabulary with increasing precision • use the standard forms of English: nouns, pronouns, adjectives, adverbs, prepositions, connectives and verb tenses

Notes

Parts of speech
Nouns

Common, proper and collective nouns

Definitions

- **Nouns** are words used to name people, places, things, feelings or ideas.
- **Common nouns** name general people, places and things.

  Example:

  'The **man** reading a **book** in the **park** had **sunglasses** on to protect his **eyes** from the **glare** of the **sun**.'

- **Proper nouns** are used to name specific people, places or things. They begin with capital letters.

  Example:

  '**Dave Simpson** sat in **Kings Park**, wearing his new sunglasses and reading the latest book by **Michelle Smith**.'

- **Collective nouns** are used to define a group of objects, people, animals, inanimate things, or concepts.

  Example:

  family, herd, flock, group, team and **class**

Explanation

- The word 'noun' comes from the Latin 'nomen', which means 'name'. Some words can be a noun, verb, or adjective, depending on how that word is used.

  Example:

  'The bank hired an extra **guard** (noun) to **guard** (verb) the safe.'

- Proper nouns are capitalised. Common and collective nouns are not capitalised unless they begin a sentence or start a title. Some nouns that would appear to need capitalisation, such as the names of seasons (winter, spring, autumn, summer) are no longer capitalised because, through long usage, they have come to be considered common nouns. Cardinal directions (north, south, east, and west), words for relatives (mum, uncle—unless used as part of the name, such as Uncle Fred) and names of some subject areas (maths, science) are also no longer considered proper nouns.

- A collective noun is a single 'thing' made up of more than one person or thing. A committee, team, or family cannot consist of one member; at least two people must compose the unit. Each collective noun can be singular or plural, depending on the sense of the sentence. When referring to the collective group, a singular verb is used.

Example:

'The team **is** flying to Melbourne for the finals.'

In this example, all members of the collective noun are doing the same thing at the same time. However, when referring to the individual members of the team acting, the plural can be used.

Example:

'The team **are** going **their** separate ways.'

- There are specific collective nouns for types of animals.

  Example:

  a **murder** of crows or a **parliament** of rooks

Worksheet information

- Give all pupils a copy of the worksheet and read the definitions with them. Explain the worksheet requirements and allow pupils to read the story and identify the different kinds of nouns. They then write these into the appropriate section of the apartment outline. Pupils then use a similar format to draw an outline of a favourite film, holiday or story with three sections and fill the outline with common, collective and proper nouns. Pupils may wish to do this on the back of the worksheet if there is not enough room in the space provided.

Ideas for further practice

- Pupils can try to describe their family without using nouns, or tell a friend about a film without using any nouns.

- Pupils form groups of three, each group with a sheet of paper. Pupils write proper nouns on the top of the sheet, fold so the words are covered, and pass it to the person next to them. Repeat with two common and two proper nouns. Pupils then open the paper and create a funny story using the six nouns on their piece of paper.

Answers

1. Common nouns: entrance, flats, apartments, stairs, flat, door, furniture, stereo, cat, sofa, fridge, food, banana, juice, television.

   Collective nouns: crowd, block, police, gang, flights, bunch, team

   Proper nouns: Asha, Cranston, Roxy, Cranston Cowboys, Rowtown Roosters

2. Teacher check

Nouns

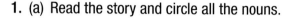

Common nouns name *general* people, places and things, ***proper nouns*** name *particular* people, places and things, and ***collective nouns*** name *groups* of people, places and things.

For example: That **herd** (collective noun) of **elephants** (common noun) was last seen in **February** (proper noun).

1. (a) Read the story and circle all the nouns.

> As Asha walked through Cranston, she saw a crowd at the entrance to her block of flats. The police were there, too. Someone told her a gang had robbed some apartments. She leapt up the two flights of stairs to her flat and opened the door very slowly. Everything was where it should be; the furniture was there, the stereo was there and Roxy, the cat, was asleep on the sofa. And best of all, the fridge full of food was safe and sound! She grabbed a banana from the bunch, some juice, and sat down in front of the television to watch her favourite team, the Cranston Cowboys, play the Rowtown Roosters.

(b) Fill in the apartment block with nouns from the story.

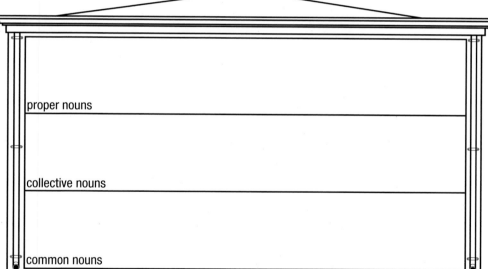

proper nouns

collective nouns

common nouns

2. Draw an outline of a shape to represent a favourite film, holiday or story. Divide it into three parts. In one part write the collective nouns from the film, story or holiday, in another the proper nouns, and in the last part, the common nouns.

Parts of speech

Nouns

Focus

Abstract nouns, gender, count and non-count nouns

Definitions

- **Abstract nouns** are the names of things that we cannot see, hear, touch or smell; things that can be thought about or experienced, such as ideas, characteristics, or qualities. The opposite of abstract nouns are concrete nouns, which name things that exist physically.

- **Masculine nouns** are nouns used to describe something male, as opposed to feminine or neuter.

- **Feminine nouns** are nouns used to describe something female, as opposed to masculine or neuter.

- **Common nouns** can be used for both males and females, such as **cousin**, **teenager**, **teacher**, **doctor**, **cook**, **pupil**, **parent**, **friend**, **relation**, **leader**.

- **Neuter nouns** name things without animal life, which are neither male nor female, such as **box**, **book**, **chair**, **broom** and **table**.

- **Count nouns** are things which can be counted and can form plurals such as **bean**, **sheet, girl** and **meeting**.

- **Non-count nouns** (also called **mass** or **uncount nouns**) name things that cannot be counted, such as **electricity**, **homework**, **weather** and **water**.

Explanation

- In language, gender is the classification of nouns according to sex. There are four genders in the English language; feminine (representing females), masculine (representing males), common (for use with either males or females) and neuter (for inanimate objects). Unlike most European languages, where the majority of nouns are either masculine or feminine, in English most nouns are either neuter or common. Many gender nouns for people that were traditionally masculine or feminine are now being replaced by common nouns, such as 'flight attendant' instead of 'air hostess', or 'firefighter' instead of 'fireman'.

- Non-count nouns are often thought of as wholes and usually have no plurals. Count nouns can be pluralised, usually by adding an 's', and 'a', 'an', 'many' or a number can be used before them. For non-count nouns, 'some', rather than 'a', 'an', or 'many', is used in front of them.

Worksheet information

- Discuss the different types of nouns the pupils are familiar with. Read the explanation about count and non-count nouns. Read the shopping list with them and make a list on the board of other count and non-count nouns. If they are having difficulty identifying non-count nouns, suggest they try adding 's' to the end, or putting 'a' etc. before it to see if it makes sense. Pupils complete the worksheet, writing their shopping list on a separate sheet of paper.

Ideas for further practice

- <http://web2.uvcs.uvic.ca/elc/studyzone/330/grammar/mass.htm> provides an explanation of ways to count non-count nouns and exercises to practise the skill.

- There are a number of websites with interactive noun activities. Be aware that many of the grammar sites on the Internet are aimed at adults learning English as a second language, and may contain adult concepts.

Answers

1. Count nouns: (6) apples, bananas, strawberries, oranges, ATM, drycleaners

   Non-count nouns: (10) fruit, beef, flour, salt, milk, butter, honey, lemonade, cash, clothing

2. furniture: chair (c), teacher: staff (nc), shorts: clothing (nc), sandwiches: food (nc), jewellery: necklace (c), art: painting (c), music: song (c), money: coin (c), suitcase: luggage (nc), apples: fruit (nc)

3.

A	H	A	T	E	Y	W	I	S
H	S	U	O	R	E	N	E	G
S	H	S	S	E	C	C	U	S
E	D	N	A	B	S	U	H	J
H	H	O	N	E	S	T	Y	O
N	O	M	L	A	C	F	Q	T
C	O	W	A	R	D	I	C	E
P	R	I	N	C	E	O	Z	F

bravery/cowardice; wife/husband; love/hate; failure/success; restless/calm; stingy/generous; dishonesty/honesty; princess/prince

4. Teacher check

Numerous nouns

Most nouns are *count nouns*. They name things that can be counted, such as trees and shoes.

Non-count (uncount) nouns name things that cannot be counted, like water and music. It is not possible to add 's' to most non-count nouns, nor to have 'a' or 'an' before them.

Many non-count nouns are also *collective nouns*, such as furniture, or *abstract nouns* which name ideas, feelings and qualities, such as happiness and wealth.

NOUNS

1. Write the number of count and non-count nouns in the shopping list.

SHOPPING LIST
- FRUIT - APPLES, BANANAS, STRAWBERRIES, ORANGES
- BEEF
- FLOUR, SALT
- MILK AND BUTTER
- HONEY
- LEMONADE

DON'T FORGET - GET SOME CASH FROM THE ATM AND PICK UP CLOTHING FROM THE DRY-CLEANERS

Count: ◯   Non-count: ◯

2. Write the matching count or uncount nouns and add 'c' or 'nc' after each word.

luggage	clothing	food	fruit
necklace	song	coin	staff
painting	chair		

furniture _____

teacher _____

shorts _____

sandwiches _____

jewellery _____

art _____

music _____

money _____

suitcase _____

apples _____

3. Find and write the opposites of these abstract and gender nouns in the wordsearch.

bravery _____

wife _____

love _____

failure _____

restless _____

stingy _____

dishonesty _____

princess _____

A	H	A	T	E	Y	W	I	S
H	S	U	O	R	E	N	E	G
S	H	S	S	E	C	C	U	S
E	D	N	A	B	S	U	H	J
H	H	O	N	E	S	T	Y	O
N	O	M	L	A	C	F	Q	T
C	O	W	A	R	D	I	C	E
P	R	I	N	C	E	O	Z	F

4. Write your own shopping list with count, non-count and collective nouns on a separate sheet of paper.

Parts of speech

Verbs

Focus

Finite verbs, the verbs *to be* and *to have*

Definition

- **Verbs** are words which show actions or states of being or having.

  Example:

  The boy next to me **copied** *my answers onto his test paper. (action)*

  She **is** *the coolest girl in the class. (being)*

  Our next-door neighbours **have** *a holiday home at the beach. (having)*

Explanation

- Verbs must have someone or something 'doing' the action, **being** or **having**. This is the subject of the sentence. In the examples above, the subjects of each sentence are **The boy**, **She** and **Our next-door neighbours**.

- Verbs are the most important parts of a sentence. Every sentence must contain a verb. Verbs can be singular or plural, depending on the number of the subject.

  Verbs have different tenses (e.g. past, present and future).

- Verbs can be finite or non-finite.

  Finite verbs change in form to match their subject or to indicate tense.

  Example:

  go, goes, went

  Non-finite verbs do not change. They include:

  present participles; for example, **walking**

  past participles; for example, **walked**

  infinitives; for example, to **walk**

- Many verbs have more than one part. Pupils will be very familiar with verbs which contain 'is', such as 'is hoping', 'am' (am collecting) , 'was' (was completing), 'were' (were playing), 'will' (will write), 'had' (had played) etc. These smaller words which form parts of verbs are called auxiliary verbs.

Worksheet information

- Ask pupils to read the definition and then discuss it with the class. Ask pupils to give examples of verbs, either from their own writing or class reading books.

- Once pupils have highlighted the verbs, check them

together. Explain verbs which have more than one part such as 'can be' and 'have found'. Explain that some verbs have 'to' at the front such as 'to fit' and 'to do'. These are types of verbs called 'infinitives'.

- With all the verbs highlighted, pupils will be able to complete Question 2 independently as well as Question 3. Ensure that pupils read their completed sentences through to see if they make sense before writing answers for Question 3.

Ideas for further practice

- Pupils write a report about an animal or unusual plant. The beginning of the report should use verbs of 'being' such as 'is' and 'are'; other sentences should include verbs of 'having' and verbs of action.

- Pupils write a short script for an action hero (using action verbs of course), to tell what he or she does.

- As a class, create a series of movements to accompany a piece of music. Write the instructions on a large sheet of cardboard and ensure that they include verbs of action.

Answers

1. (a) Teacher check

   (b) go, find, am, try, to fit (infinitive), make, is, to do (infinitive), chatter, give, sounds, memorise, cart, seems, wait, is, have found, see, can be

2. (a) Answers will vary but will include four of the following words: go, find, am, try, make, is, chatter, give, sounds, memorise, cart, seems, wait, is, see

   (b) Answers will be one of the following: am, is, can be

   (c) have found

   (d) Answers will vary but should include three of the following: to fit, to do, have found, can be

3. Answers may vary but some suggestions are:

   (a) can be/will be/is/may be

   (b) takes/will take, know/remember

   (c) have/will have

   (d) gives/assigns/will give, have/will have

Verbs

A **verb** is a word which shows actions, or states of *being* or *having*.

1. (a) Read the poem below then highlight all the verbs.

> Whenever I go to a new school, I find it really hard.
>
> New faces, new places. I am always on guard.
>
> New teachers, new friends. I try so hard to fit in.
>
> More pupils, loudspeakers. They make such a din.
>
> New subjects, more homework. There is always so much to do.
>
> Pupils chatter and teachers give orders. It sounds like a zoo.
>
> I memorise the timetable and cart my books around.
>
> Sometimes it seems too much. But wait! Who is this I have found?
>
> I see a friendly, familiar face. Someone from my old school.
>
> Perhaps life can be an adventure and maybe a little less cruel!

(b) Write the verbs below, in the order you found them. Be careful! Some may have more than one word.

_____

_____

_____

2. Write examples of verbs from the text:

(a) four one-word verbs _____

_____

(b) one verb of 'being' _____

(c) one verb of 'having' _____

(d) three two-word verbs _____

_____

3. Complete the sentences by adding a suitable verb. Some verbs may have more than one part.

(a) Secondary school _____ difficult when you first go there.

(b) It _____ some time before you are used to the timetable

and _____ where to go for each lesson.

(c) At secondary school, you _____ more than one teacher.

(d) Each teacher of each different subject _____

homework so that you _____ a lot more homework

to do.

Parts of speech

Verbs

Focus

Command verbs (imperatives)

Definition

- Verbs are words which show actions or states of being or having.
- A **command verb** is used to order, command or instruct.

  Example:

  > **Read** the text and then **answer** the questions in complete sentences.

  > **Arrange** the flowers in a vase and **place** the vase on the table.

  > **Brush** your teeth and **rinse** your mouth with mouthwash.

Explanation

- Verbs can describe actions or states of 'being' or 'having'. They must have someone or something 'doing' the action or 'being' or 'having'.
- Command verbs are commonly used when writing procedures such as recipes or science experiments and are often the first word in the sentence.
- Command verbs do not have a stated subject (anyone or anything doing the action). It is understand that the person doing the action is 'you'.

Worksheet information

- Allow the pupils to read the text independently, offering assistance if required. Other verbs are contained in the text as well but for the purpose of the exercises on the pupil page, they have not been included in any answers.
- Read the definition together and discuss. Give examples of other command verbs and ask pupils to offer suggestions as well. Identify one or two in the text to assist the pupils if necessary.

- When finding command verbs to complete Question 1, pupils need to be aware that some are not at the beginning of the sentence but in the middle. Pupils may wish to identify all the verbs before selecting those which are command verbs and writing them in the box.
- As a group, discuss the type of instructions which could be written to answer Question 2.

Ideas for further practice

- Orally, pupils repeat commands given by parents at home.
- Pupils write instructions for using a new computer program using command verbs.

Example:

> 'Open the program by double clicking on the icon. Go to ...'

- Read the instructions and rules of a board or card game to see whether command verbs have been used.

Answers

1. Wear, Organise, Find, talk, ask, Offer, Join, Avoid, try, Invite, buy, hire, have, go

2. Teacher check

Command verbs

1. (a) Read the text below.

> *Many people are shy and feel uncomfortable at parties or other social gatherings. The following ideas may help you cope with meeting new people (and you might even have fun!).*
>
> - *Wear your best, most comfortable gear so that you look and feel great.*
>
> - *Organise a lift home with a parent or parent of a friend at a suitable time. If you think that you can only cope with two hours of socialising, then it's better to leave at that time rather than hang around bored or uncomfortable for another hour or two.*
>
> - *Find a person in a group of people you know and talk with him or her. If there is anyone in the group that you don't know, ask that person a few questions to get to know them. You can tell some jokes too (if you know any good ones)!*
>
> - *Offer to carry some plates of food around to hand out to guests. You will get to meet lots of people and they will be happy to see you because you are bringing them food! The person holding the party will be grateful for your help and the time will pass quickly.*
>
> - *Join in as many games as you can, as well as any dancing and singing. It helps the time to pass quickly and you get to know more people and have fun.*
>
> - *Avoid doing anything really silly that might make you the centre of attention. You want to fit in, not be the odd one out!*
>
> - *Lastly, try organising a simple party of your own with a few close friends. Invite a few extra people you would like to get to know, buy some 'munchies', hire some DVDs, have some CDs of music ready to listen to and go for it!*

VERBS

Command verbs are used to order, command or give instructions. They are commonly used at the beginning of sentences in a procedure.

(b) Write all the command verbs from the text in the box below. Some are at the beginning of a sentence.

2. Use the space below to write some instructions for a dance using command verbs.

_____

_____

_____

_____

Parts of speech

Verbs

VERBS

Focus

Past, present and future tense (including irregular verbs)

Auxiliary verbs

Definitions

- Verbs are words which show actions or states of being or having.
- **Verb tense** shows whether the action of the verb occurs in the present, the past or the future.
- **Auxiliary verbs** are small verbs, often a form of the verb 'to be' or 'to have', that combine with another verb to form a compound verb.

  Example:

  *I **will** study medicine while I **am** living in America.*

Explanation

- There are three basic verb tenses—past, present and future. These tenses are often formed using an auxiliary or helping verb such as, 'is', 'can', 'had' and 'will'.

  Example:

  *Boris **is depositing** his daily catch on the doorstep as a prize for his mistress. (present tense)*

  *The surfer **had ploughed** through the waves and **skimmed** past the rocks. (past tense)*

  *Perhaps one day, we **will commute** without causing pollution. (future tense)*

- Many verbs in the past tense end in **-ed**. Many present tense verbs end in **-s** or **-es**.
- In the sentences above, 'is', 'had' and 'will' are auxiliary verbs, with 'is' forming part of the present tense verb, 'had' used as part of the past tense and 'will' forming part of a future tense verb.
- Most verb tense forms are regular (they have **-ed**, **-es** or add auxiliary verbs such as 'is' and 'will' to make the correct tense), but many are irregular.

  Example:

  *They **are drawing** an impressionist picture. (present tense)*

  *They **drew** an impressionist picture. (past tense)*

  Irregular verbs include be/was/were; begin/began; do/did; grow/grew; get/got; drink/drank; choose/chose and make/made.

  A more detailed list can be found by searching the Internet.

Worksheet information

- Read the explanation with the pupils and discuss. Give some examples if necessary, especially simple verb tenses; such as those which end with **-s** (present tense) and **-ed** (past tense).
- Discuss verbs and identify some in the text. Pupils can then complete Question 1.

  Check answers and ensure that pupils understand the different tenses before proceeding.

- Remind the pupils about irregular verbs and allow them to complete Question 3. Check answers as a class and suggest other examples of irregular verbs.

Ideas for further practice

- Rewrite sentences to change them from one tense to another.
- Read through previous writing efforts and find occasions when the tense of a verb was incorrect or the tense was inconsistent throughout the piece of work.
- Create rhymes which aid in remembering the tense of irregular verbs.

  Example:

  Fly is now, flew was before

  But in the future, 'will' comes to the fore.

Answers

1. saw, was, made, live, was, got, flew, hid, cried, to make (infinitive), did (not) hear, returned, made, made, placed, cried, make, heard, shone, made, burst, became, died, were unharmed, had disappeared, remained, moved, emerged, grew, collected, placed, flew, placed, flew, to live (infinitive), grows, flies, is reborn

Answers include:

2. (a) is returning/return, will return/will have returned
   (b) cry/cries/is/are crying, will cry
   (c) emerge/emerges/is/am/are emerging, will emerge
   (d) was reborn, will be reborn
3. (a) see/sees/can see/is/are seeing, will see
   (b) flew/has/have flown/was/were flying, will fly
   (c) make/makes/is/am/are making, will make
   (d) become/becomes/is/am/are becoming, will become
   (e) shine/shines/is/am/are shining, will shine
   (f) grew/has/had grown/was grown, will grow

Verb tense

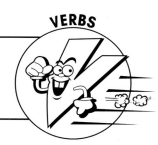

Verb tense can tell about what happened in the past, what is happening in the present or what will happen in the future. Many verbs have more than one part.

For example: *are*, *is* and *will* are used to complete the verb.

1. Read the legend about the phoenix and underline all the verbs.

> Long ago, the sun saw a large red and gold bird. It was so beautiful that the sun made him live forever.
>
> At first the phoenix was very happy, but eventually he got old and tired. So he flew away and hid in the desert all alone. He cried to the sun to make him young and strong again, but the sun did not hear him.
>
> The phoenix returned home and made a nest in a tall palm tree. He made an egg from myrrh and placed it in the nest. He cried out to the sun again, 'Please, glorious sun, make me young and strong again!' This time the sun heard him and shone its burning rays down on the Earth. The rays made the tree burst into flame and the phoenix became a big ball of fire.
>
> When the flames died down, the tree and nest were unharmed but the phoenix had disappeared. Only a pile of ash remained. Soon the ash moved and a young phoenix emerged. It quickly grew to the size of a mature phoenix. Then it collected the ashes, placed them inside the egg and flew away with it. The phoenix placed the egg on the altar of the sun and flew back to live in the desert. Every five hundred years, when it grows old, the phoenix flies back to the old palm tree and is reborn from the ashes.

2. Complete the table for these words from the text.

	Past tense	Present tense	Future tense
(a)	returned		
(b)	cried		
(c)	emerged		
(d)		is reborn	

3. Some verb tenses are irregular. They do not add *-s* or *-es* for present tense, or *-ed* for past tense. Some words change completely. Write irregular verbs from the text in different tenses.

	Past tense	Present tense	Future tense
(a)	saw		
(b)		flies	
(c)	made		
(d)	became		
(e)	shone		
(f)		grows	

Parts of speech

Adjectives

Focus

Common and proper adjectives

Definitions

- An **adjective** is a describing word. It adds meaning to or changes the meaning of a noun or a pronoun.

  Example:

  *My sister bought a **stylish linen** shirt. (describes the noun, 'shirt')*

  *This film is **boring**. (describes the noun, 'film')*
  Note: The adjective does not always come before the noun.

  *He is **generous**. (describes the pronoun, 'He')*

- **Proper adjectives** are made from proper nouns.

  Example:

  ***American** flag*

  They usually begin with an initial capital letter. Proper adjectives are also called 'adjectives of origin'.

Explanation

- The use of suitable adjectives not only makes written or spoken language more interesting, it gives the reader or listener a clearer understanding.

Worksheet information

- Discuss adjectives using the information and examples at the top of page 13. Ask pupils for further examples of common and proper adjectives.

- Pupils individually or as a group identify the adjectives and the nouns or pronouns they describe in the text in 1(a). Guide them to ask questions such as 'What kind?' in front of the noun to help their identification. Afterwards, discuss how the adjectives added to the appeal of that home.

- If possible, provide pupils with some sample advertisements from newspapers or the Internet that use adjectives to add to their appeal and provide information. The class could brainstorm to list adjectives they could use in their advertisement. Point out that it is common to use more than one adjective to describe something. Compare pupils' advertisements and discuss the suitability of their choices. Ask 'Did that adjective give the reader a clearer picture of the home's features? Did it sound appealing?'

- Pupils could work in pairs to complete Question 2, helping each other to sort their adjectives. This activity is designed to make pupils aware of the different types of adjectives. Compare answers with those of other class members.

Ideas for further practice

- Write a paragraph using adjectives to make something more appealing to sell; e.g. a sporting item, a car, a pet or a household appliance.

- Plan a restaurant menu for breakfast, lunch or dinner using adjectives to make the food appealing to a diner.

- Use the adjectives from Question 2 to write in the correct order. This is usually size, age, shape, quality, colour, material, origin, purpose; e.g. large, old, ceramic, German, drinking mug. A good way to decide is to say the adjectives aloud and hear what sounds correct. Note that while it is common to use more than one adjective to describe something, usually no more than three or four are used.

Answers

1. (a) ***Rare*** chance to purchase ***huge*** home with ***stunning ocean*** views. They are ***spectacular***. ***Multi-storey***, ***five-bedroom***, ***three-bathroom*** mansion with ***modern***, ***spacious*** kitchen and ***open-plan***, ***living*** areas. ***French*** doors leading onto ***large*** patio, ***enchanting*** garden and ***double*** garage. Close to ***public*** transport.

   (b) Teacher check

2. Adjectives from advertisement: Possible answers:
   Quality – rare, stunning, spectacular, modern, spacious, enchanting, double
   Purpose – multi-storey, five-bedroom, three-bathroom, open-plan, living, public
   Size – huge, large
   Material/Substance – ocean
   Origin – French

   Teacher check other adjectives

Adjectives

Adjectives are words that describe nouns or pronouns. They help make writing clearer and more interesting for the reader.

For example: The *large, red-spotted* bird soared into the *blue* sky.

Proper adjectives are made from proper nouns and have a capital letter.

For example: The *German* chef cooked a schnitzel.

1. Read the advertisement about the house for sale. Notice how adjectives have been used to make the house appealing to a buyer and to provide information about its features.

    (a) Highlight the words that have been used as adjectives and underline the noun or pronoun they describe.

    (b) Make up your own 'House for sale' advertisement. Brainstorm to list adjectives that can be used to make the house appealing to a buyer and to provide information about its features.

FOR SALE

Open today 1.30–2.30
2 Coastal Drive, Southby

Rare chance to purchase huge home with stunning ocean views. They are spectacular. Multi-storey, five-bedroom, three-bathroom mansion with modern, spacious kitchen and open-plan living areas. French doors leading onto large patio, enchanting garden and double garage. Close to public transport.

2. Examples of ways to classify adjectives have been given below. Now sort the adjectives from the above advertisement and from yours into the table.

Quality	Purpose	Size	Shape
sharp	work (clothes)	gigantic	circular
Age	**Colour**	**Material/Substance**	**Origin**
old	purple	metallic	Greek

Parts of speech
Adjectives

Focus

Comparative and superlative adjectives

Definitions

- **Comparative adjectives** are used to compare two things, usually by adding the suffix *er*.

  Example:

  fast, faster

- **Superlative adjectives** are used to compare more than two things usually by adding the suffix *est*.

  Example:

  fast, fastest

Explanation

- If the adjective has two or more syllables, 'more' or 'most' is usually added before the adjective.

  Example:

  valuable, more valuable, most valuable

- If the adjective of two or more syllables ends in 'y', 'y' changes to 'i' and *er* or *est* is usually used.

  Example:

  silly, sillier, silliest

- Some comparative and superlative adjectives are irregular.

  Example:

  bad, worse, worst

  good, better, best

Worksheet information

- Use the information at the top of page 15 to discuss how *er* or *est* or 'more' or 'most' are added to adjectives to compare things. Note how 'the' is often used before the superlative form (**the** coldest climate).

- Pupils read the paragraph in Activity 1, highlighting the adjectives that compare. Discuss those that use *er* and *est*, those that use 'more' and 'most' and the irregular form of 'bad', 'worse', 'worst' and 'good', 'better' and 'best'.

- To complete Activity 2, pupils need to identify when to add *er*, *est*, 'more' or 'most' to an adjective. Use the examples in the Explanation section above about hints to decide which form to choose. Sometimes the best way is to say the choices out loud and hear what sounds correct. Dictionaries could also be used.

- Activity 3 provides practice at identifying the correct comparative or superlative form of adjectives in context. Compare answers when complete to check for correctness. Note: The last line includes the irregular form of bad, worse, worst, which may need extra discussion.

Ideas for further practice

- In pairs, pupils prepare short oral or written reports of facts that compare animals, places, characters/people from fiction and nonfiction, using the correct comparative and superlative adjectives.

Answers

1. Some of the world's **worst** natural disasters have been caused by volcanic eruptions. The **most powerful** in modern history occurred in 1815, when Mt Tambora in Indonesia erupted, killing 92 000 people. Volcanic ash blocking the sunlight caused **cooler** conditions the following summer in nearby countries. The **noisiest** eruption occurred in 1883 with the **loudest** sound ever heard on Earth, caused by the explosion of the volcanic island of Krakatoa in Indonesia. Although 29 000 died in the Mt Pelee eruption in the West Indies in 1902, two lucky people survived. One lived on the outskirts of town. Even **luckier** was a prisoner who had a **better** position—an underground prison cell! A **more famous** eruption was that of Mt Vesuvius in Italy, in 79 BCE. It completely buried the towns of Pompeii, Herculaneum and Stabiae.

2. (a) livelier, liveliest
   (b) shallower, shallowest
   (c) more childish, most childish
   (d) more mysterious, most mysterious
   (e) thinner, thinnest
   (f) wealthier, wealthiest
   (g) better, best

3. The Taj Mahal in India is considered by many people to be the **most beautiful** building in the world. It is made from the **finest** white marble inlaid with semiprecious stones. It looks stunning in the moonlight as it has a golden glow. At sunset it looks **more stunning** as it appears pure white. But it is the **most stunning** at sunrise when it appears a dusky pink. The Taj Mahal is one of the **most popular** tourist attractions in the world. However, the millions of visitors walking through it have eroded some of the marble. Unfortunately, this will become a **worse** problem as time goes by.

Comparatives and superlatives

When we compare two things, we change the adjective, usually by adding *er*.
For example: Finland has a cold climate but the Arctic's is cold*er*.
                 This is called the **comparative**.

When we compare three or more things, we change the adjective, usually by adding *est*.
For example: The Antarctic has the cold*est* climate of all.
                 This is called the **superlative**.

The words **more** or **most** are used before some adjectives to compare things.
For example: spectacular, **more** spectacular, **most** spectacular

1. Read the paragraph below about natural disasters. Highlight the adjectives that are used to compare.

Some of the world's worst natural disasters have been caused by volcanic eruptions. The most powerful in modern history occurred in 1815, when Mt Tambora in Indonesia erupted, killing 92 000 people. Volcanic ash blocking the sunlight caused cooler conditions the following summer in nearby countries. The noisiest eruption occurred in 1883 with the loudest sound ever heard on Earth, caused by the explosion of the volcanic island of Krakatoa in Indonesia. Although 29 000 died in the Mt Pelee eruption in the West Indies in 1902, two lucky people survived. One lived on the outskirts of town. Even luckier was a prisoner who had a better position—an underground prison cell! A more famous eruption was that of Mt Vesuvius in Italy, in 79 BCE. It completely buried the towns of Pompeii, Herculaneum and Stabiae.

2. Complete the table below, changing the adjectives by adding *er*, *est*, *more* or *most*. (One of them is an irregular adjective which doesn't use *er*, *est*, *more* or *most*.)
   Remember to change the *y* to *i* when adding *er* or *est* to some words.

Adjective	Comparative adjective	Superlative adjective
(a) lively		
(b) shallow		
(c) childish		
(d) mysterious		
(e) thin		
(f) wealthy		
(g) good		

3. Change the adjectives in bold print to the correct form, by neatly printing the words above the errors.

*The Taj Mahal in India is considered by many people to be the **beautifullest** building in the world. It is made from the **finer** white marble inlaid with semiprecious stones. It looks stunning in the moonlight as it has a golden glow. At sunset it looks **stunninger** as it appears pure white. But it is the **stunningest** at sunrise when it appears a dusky pink. The Taj Mahal is one of the most **popularest** tourist attractions in the world. However, the millions of visitors walking through it have eroded some of the marble. Unfortunately, this will become a **badder** problem as time goes by.*

Parts of speech
Adjectives

Focus

Adjectival phrases and clauses

Definitions

- An **adjective** is a describing word that adds meaning to or changes the meaning of a noun or pronoun (refer to page 12 for examples).

- An **adjectival phrase** is a group of words used like an adjective to describe a noun or pronoun. It does not contain a verb with a subject.

  Example:

  > Who is the <u>coach</u> **with the loud voice**?

  The noun the phrase describes is underlined. Note: The adjectival phrase usually comes after the noun.

- An **adjectival clause** is a group of words containing at least one verb with a subject that does the work of an adjective; often starting with a relative pronoun.

  Example:

  > The <u>coach</u> **who** is **blowing the whistle** wants to stop the game.

  The noun the clause describes is underlined. The verb is circled.

  NOTE: The adjectival clause comes directly after the noun.

Explanation

- Adjectival phrases and clauses make written and spoken language more interesting and meaning clearer. A group of words rather than one or two adjectives can often be a more interesting, informative or precise way of describing a noun or pronoun.

- Although adjectival phrases and clauses can describe pronouns, all the examples given on the pupil page describe nouns because they are more common. An example describing a pronoun is:

  > <u>He</u>, who hates spiders, actually picked one up.

Worksheet information

- Use the information above to explain adjectival phrases and clauses and how they can often provide more information than one adjective. Emphasise that a phrase does not contain a verb with a subject

and that an adjectival phrase often begins with a preposition such as 'with' or 'on' (refer to pages 32 to 33 for extra information about prepositions). A clause does contain a verb with a subject and an adjectival clause often begins with a relative pronoun such as 'who' or 'which'.

- Pupils need to be sure to identify the noun or pronoun being described so they do not confuse adjectival phrases and clauses with adverbial phrases and clauses, which describe verbs (refer to pages 18 to 21 for extra information). The activities on page 17 provide an introduction to the concept as well as opportunities for pupils to write their own adjectival phrases and clauses.

Ideas for further practice

- In pairs or individually, pupils compile adjectival phrases, beginning with a preposition, describing a noun or pronoun and write them on cards. They place the cards face down, choose one and then make up a complete sentence using that phrase. Pupils can swap cards with other pairs.

- In pairs or individually, pupils compile adjectival clauses beginning with a relative pronoun describing a noun or pronoun and write them on cards. They place the cards face down, choose one and then make up a complete sentence using that clause. Pupils can swap cards with other pairs.

Answers

1. (a) on duty
   (b) with the new extension ladder
   (c) with the iron rungs
   (d) with waterbombs
   (e) with the most experience
   (f) with a clever disguise

2. Teacher check

3. Verbs are in bold
   (a) which **tours** the Kruger National Park
   (b) which **is** one of the oldest and largest in Africa
   (c) which **flow** all year round
   (d) who **are** very experienced
   (e) whose habitat **lies** in the park
   (f) who **take** photographs from the vehicles

4. Teacher check

Adjectival phrases and clauses

An **adjectival phrase** is a group of words used like an adjective to describe a noun or pronoun. It does not contain a verb with a subject. It usually comes after the noun or pronoun.

1. Highlight the adjectival phrase in each sentence. The noun it describes is underlined.

   (a) The <u>firefighters</u> on duty hurried to their vehicles and raced to the fire.

   (b) The <u>fire truck</u> with the new extension ladder left the fire station first.

   (c) They raised the <u>ladder</u> with the iron rungs and placed it against the building.

   (d) The <u>helicopters</u> with waterbombs helped extinguish the flames.

   (e) The <u>firefighters</u> with the most experience checked the burnt-out building.

   (f) An <u>onlooker</u> with a clever disguise ventured into the smouldering ruins.

2. Add a suitable adjectival phrase to describe the noun that is underlined.

   (a) The <u>arsonist</u> _____ was seen nearby.

   (b) A <u>person</u> _____ saw him running.

   (c) His hiding place was some <u>bushes</u> _____.

   (d) A small <u>dog</u> _____ sniffed him out.

   (e) The <u>police</u> _____ led him away.

An **adjectival clause** is a group of words used like an adjective to describe a noun or pronoun. It contains a verb with a subject. It usually comes after the noun or pronoun.

3. Highlight the adjectival clause in each sentence and circle the verb it contains. The noun the clause describes is underlined.

   (a) The African <u>safari</u> which tours the Kruger National Park commences on Friday.

   (b) The <u>Kruger National Park</u> which is one of the oldest and largest in Africa attracts over one million visitors a year.

   (c) It has six major <u>rivers</u> which flow all year round.

   (d) The tour <u>guides</u> who are very experienced make your trip enjoyable.

   (e) Most of the <u>animals</u> whose habitat lies in the park are used to tourists in vehicles.

   (f) They are also used to <u>tourists</u> who take photographs from the vehicles.

4. Add a suitable adjectival clause to describe the noun that is underlined. Circle the verb you use in each clause.

   (a) A bull <u>elephant</u> _____ ignored us.

   (b) A young <u>impala</u> _____ ran to its mother.

   (c) Our <u>4WD</u> _____ avoided potholes.

   (d) My <u>companion</u> _____ saw a lion.

   (e) The <u>lion</u> _____ roared.

Parts of speech

Adverbs

Focus

Common adverbs of manner, time, place and frequency

Definition

- An **adverb** is a word that adds information, usually to a verb, and can tell how (manner), when (time), where (place) and the frequency (how often) that something happens.

  Example:

  > **Today** (time), the research team off the Western Australian coast **proudly** (manner) announced that they had located HMAS Sydney **there** (place) and claimed they had **never** (frequency) doubted their eventual success.

  Note: Adverbs can modify (add information to) any words that are not nouns or pronouns. (These are modified by adjectives.)

Explanation

- Adverbs can clarify meaning by telling more about the action, allowing for greater precision and adding interest to writing.

- Pupils should be reminded that adding appropriate adverbs will make their speaking and writing more informative, precise and interesting.

- Adverbs can be used to describe the **frequency** or **duration** of an occurrence.

  Example:

  > daily, forever

  They can also describe the **extent** of something occurring.

  Example:

  > absolutely, quite

  They can be interrogative.

  Example:

  > how, when, where, why

Worksheet information

- After pupils have read the text, ask them to work out what the words in **italics** have in common. Remind them that verbs tell about something someone does or an occurrence (see pages 6–11).

- Explain that adverbs can tell **how** (manner), **when** (time) or **where** (place) something happens. We need to identify the verbs before trying to find the adverbs.

  Note: There are compound verbs included in the text.

- Model the process of identifying the adverbs by asking **how**, **when** and **where** of the verb. Some pupils will need to have the process modelled numerous times before they are able to complete Question 2 independently.

- Question 3 can be used to illustrate how more informative and precise adverbs make communication.

- Question 4 introduces interrogative adverbs. Pupils should realise that the words, **how**, **when**, **where** and **why** are themselves adverbs. They are then required to answer the question using the same verb with an appropriate adverb. Encourage pupils to try to select the 'best' adverb for each of their sentences.

- Question 5 introduces adverbs of frequency. Encourage pupils to ask, 'How often' before the verb.

Ideas for further practice

- Pupils work in small groups to identify verbs in a page of text; to list them and write any adverbs used in the text to modify them. They can then add any other suitable adverbs.

Answers

2.

Verbs	Adverbs	Category
hold	still	time
hidden	below	place
was recorded	fortunately	manner
has been known	well	manner
are	always	time
nestled	silently	manner
to be discovered	yet	time
was	sadly	manner
believed	widely	manner
were	unfortunately	manner
succeeded	finally	time
located	cleverly	manner

3.-5. Teacher check

Adverbs

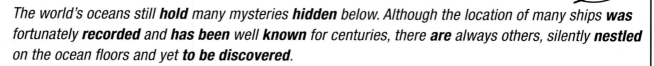

Words telling *how*, *when*, *where* or *how often* things occur are called *adverbs*.

1. Read the text.

> The world's oceans still **hold** many mysteries **hidden** below. Although the location of many ships **was** fortunately **recorded** and **has been** well **known** for centuries, there **are** always others, silently **nestled** on the ocean floors and yet **to be discovered**.
>
> One such ship **was**, sadly, HMAS Sydney, an Australian battle cruiser widely **believed** sunk off Western Australia's coast in 1941. Unfortunately, there **were** no survivors.
>
> In March 2008, a team of researchers finally **succeeded**. With sophisticated sonar equipment, they cleverly **located** the final resting place of the ship and its 645 crew.

2. Complete the chart. The verbs in the text are in **italics**. Ask the questions **how**, **when** or **where** of the verb to find the adverb. Then write 'manner' or 'time' or 'place' to describe the category.

Verb	Adverb	Category
hold	still	time

3. Write interesting adverbs to tell how shipwreck researchers could do these things.

   (a) search _____ (b) locate _____

4. The adverb in each question is underlined. Answer the question using one interesting adverb, which tells more about the verb.

   (a) <u>How</u> do ships sink?_____

   (b) <u>Where</u> are shipwrecks found?_____

   (c) <u>When</u> will some shipwrecks be found?_____

5. Chose an adverb of frequency to complete each sentence.

   seldom   **always**   **never**   **usually**   **rarely**   **often**

   (a) Some Australians _____ believed HMAS Sydney would be found.

   (b) Missing wrecks are _____ located in deep water.

   (c) Ships _____ sink with the loss of all their crew.

   (d) Locating HMAS Sydney shows that searchers should _____ give up.

Parts of speech
Adverbs

Focus

Adverbial phrases and clauses

Adverb/adjective confusion

Definitions

- An **adverb** is a word that can add information usually to a verb and can tell how (manner), when (time), where (place) or how often (frequency) something occurs.

- An **adverbial phrase** is a group of words which can be used like an adverb to modify or enhance the verb. It does not contain a verb with a subject.

  Example:

  *The ship's captain berthed his ship **after a long and hazardous voyage**.*

- An **adverbial clause** is a group of words including a verb with a subject which can be used like an adverb to modify or enhance the verb.

  Example:

  *He is setting sail **when the wind becomes more favourable**.*

  Note: Adverbs can modify any words that are not nouns or pronouns. (Adjectives modify nouns and pronouns.)

Explanation

- Adverbials can clarify meaning by telling more about the action, allowing for greater precision and adding interest to writing.

- Pupils should be reminded that adding adverbs and adverbial phrases and clauses to verbs will make their writing more informative, precise and interesting.

- In a similar way to an adverb, adverbial clauses and phrases can be used to give more information about a verb. Both clauses and phrases are groups of words, but with one major difference. A clause has a subject and a verb and can be considered a sentence within a sentence, while a phrase is a group of words. Adverbially, they both function in the same way, usually enhancing and modifying a verb.

- Adverbs can modify not only verbs but can also modify other parts of speech. Some examples are provided below for your information. The adverbs are in italics.

  Note: Adverbs can also modify phrases, clauses and sentences.

  *I have a **very** <u>strange</u> pet. (adjective)*
  *My house is **just** <u>around</u> the corner. (preposition)*
  *We travelled for **almost** <u>four</u> hours. (determiner)*
  *He worked **really** <u>quickly</u>. (adverb)*
  *I will come **only** <u>if</u> he joins us. (conjunction)*

Worksheet information

- Although different types of adverbial phrases and clauses have been given and introduced separately on the worksheet, it is important pupils understand that using a group of words can often be a better way of telling more about a verb than just using an adverb alone.

- Question 5 is an introduction to the correct use of adjectives and adverbs, which are very often confused in speech. It is suggested that opportunities for further discussion, practice and correction at the point of error be provided.

Ideas for further practice

- Brainstorm other words that have different adjectival and adverbial forms. Pupils write or speak sentences using these pairs of words correctly.

- Model changing adjectives to adverbs, usually by adding **ly**. Discuss the spelling rules involved, including:

  After a consonant in *le* words, change *e* to *y*.

  Example:

  terrible – terribly, simple – simply

  After a vowel, just add **ly**.

  Example:

  pale – palely, brave – bravely

Answers

1. (a) about midnight – time
   (b) just in time – time
   (c) on the deck – place
   (d) an ear-piercing roar – manner
   (e) in a very professional way – manner
   (f) in every port – place

2. Teacher check

3. (a) when the children first <u>tried to paddle</u> it.
   (b) when a stiff breeze <u>is blowing</u>.
   (c) as it <u>was attempting to dock</u> in Boston.
   (d) while he <u>was serving</u> in the navy.
   (e) close to where the German ship, *Kormoran,* <u>sank</u>.
   (f) when it <u>sailed</u> the downwind leg faster than the other boats in the race

4. Teacher check

5. (a) easily, easy
   (b) proudly, proud
   (c) well, good
   (d) quickly, quick
   (e) really, real

Adverbial phrases and clauses

ADVERBS

> An *adverbial phrase* is a group of words which can be used like an adverb to add information to a verb. A phrase does not contain a verb with a subject.

1. Underline the adverbial phrase in each sentence and write if it is of *time*, *place*, *manner* or *frequency*. The verbs have been written in italics.

   (a) The aircraft carrier *was expected to sail* about midnight. _____

   (b) One member of the crew *arrived* just in time. _____

   (c) Some of the aircraft *were lined up* on the deck. _____

   (d) A jet *was landing* with an ear-piercing roar. _____

   (e) The experienced crew *worked* in a very professional way. _____

   (f) Most of the crew *had* some leave in every port. _____

2. Add a suitable adverbial phrase telling *how*, *when* or *where* about the verb.

   (a) The damaged ship *sank* _____

   (b) Some crew members *scrambled* _____

   (c) Rescuers *located* some survivors _____

> An *adverbial clause* is a group of words, including a verb with a subject, which can be used like an adverb to add information to a verb.

3. Underline the adverbial clause in each sentence and circle the verb that is included in it.

   (a) The canoe circled when the children first tried to paddle it.

   (b) I enjoy sailing when a stiff breeze is blowing.

   (c) The ship hit the wharf as it was attempting to dock in Boston.

   (d) My father visited many countries while he was serving in the navy.

   (e) *Sydney* was finally located close to where the German ship, *Kormoran,* sank.

   (f) Our small yacht won the race when it sailed the downwind leg faster than the other boats in the race.

4. Add a suitable adverbial clause to each sentence. Don't forget the verbs.

   (a) The boat sailed _____

   (b) The old sailor told stories _____

5. Adverbs or adjectives? Circle the correct words.

   (a) The New Zealand boat won **easy/easily**. It had an **easy/easily** victory.

   (b) The crew **proud/proudly** accepted the cup. They felt **proud/proudly**.

   (c) They had sailed **good/well**. It was a **good/well** race.

   (d) The yacht moved **quick/quickly.** It is **quick/quickly**.

   (e) Is that cup **real/really** made of silver? Yes, it is a **real/really** silver cup.

Parts of speech
Pronouns

Focus

Personal, indefinite and interrogative pronouns

Definitions

- A **pronoun** is a word substituted for a noun.
- A **personal pronoun** is used in place of a person or thing.
  Example:
  he, she, it, they
- An **indefinite pronoun** refers to an unspecified person or thing.
  Example:
  Anyone can come.
- **Interrogative pronouns** ask questions that give a noun or pronoun response.
  Example:
  Who is your teacher?

- The 12 **indefinite pronouns** are shown in the table below. Some refer to people and others to things.

INDEFINITE PRONOUNS			
somebody	anybody	nobody	everybody
someone	anyone	no-one	everyone
something	anything	nothing	everything

- These are the five **interrogative pronouns** all of which give a noun or pronoun response.

INTERROGATIVE PRONOUNS				
what	which	who	whom	whose

Explanation

- The use of pronouns prevents constant repetition of a noun.
- It is important for pupils to know the correct pronouns to use in the context of a particular sentence so their grammar, in speech and in writing, is accurate.
- The table below shows which personal pronoun to use:

PERSONAL PRONOUNS				
Person	Subjective	Objective	Emphatic/ Reflexive	Possessive
First singular	I	me	myself	mine
Second	you	you	yourself	yours
Third (male)	he	him	himself	his
Third (female)	she	her	herself	hers
Third (neuter)	it	it	itself	its
First plural	we	us	ourselves	ours
Second	you	you	yourselves	yours
Third	they	them	themselves	theirs

1. When the person the pronoun refers to is either the subject or object.
   Example:
   You (subject) must make it (object) for me. (object)
2. To emphasise the subject of the verb.
   Example:
   He weeded the garden himself. (emphatic pronoun)
3. To indicate that the object of the verb is the same person referred to in the subject.
   Example:
   They enjoyed themselves. (reflexive pronoun)
4. To indicate possession.
   Example:
   These goggles are yours.

Worksheet information

- Discuss the different types of pronouns so pupils are clear about the use of each.
- Pupils should read through the text at least once before filling the gaps.
- Pupils could check their answers with each other and discuss any differences.

Ideas for further practice

- Pupils create their own tables of pronouns and, in their own words, write rules for use with examples.
- Highlight individual pronouns in simple text and ask pupils to explain what type of pronoun it is and which noun it refers to.

Answers

1.
1. They	2. It	3. it	4. himself
5. Who	6. he	7. whose	8. he
9. Nobody	10. it	11. yours	12. she
13. It	14. mine	15. Everyone	16. we
17. They	18. You	19. He	20. I
21. it	22. I	23. I	24. it
25. yours	26. yours	27. I	

Pronouns

A pronoun is a word substituted for a noun.

Read the text carefully. All of the pronouns in bold print are of the correct type but are in the wrong person.

Use the clues within the text to choose the correct pronouns. Write them in the spaces provided.

The Class 6 pupils were all ready to embark on their trip to the forest. **He** _____ [1] all

boarded the bus and settled down to enjoy the journey. Before long, Claudia and Amelia began

their usual antics. A hiking boot flew down the bus. **You** _____ [2] narrowly missed Mr

Posset's balding head. This was followed quickly by an overripe banana which exploded as **they**

_____ [3] made contact with its target. Wiping **itself** _____ [4] with a

handkerchief, Mr Posset stood up. His face had turned a delicate shade of pink.

'**What** _____ [5] threw this banana?' **she** _____ [6] asked calmly, holding up its

dark brown peel. 'And **who** _____ [7] boot is this?'

As **I** _____ [8] held up the boot, his quiet voice belied his inner anger.

Everybody _____ [9] answered. 'Amelia Fendrol!

Is **he** _____ [10] **ours** _____ [11] ?'

'No, sir', **they** _____ [12] answered confidently.

'**We**'s _____ [13] not **theirs** _____ [14].' The bus had parked in a roadside picnic area.

No-one _____ [15] was silent. 'Now,' said Mr Posset, 'is someone going to own up or shall **they**

_____ [16] have a boot parade?'

The other teachers left the bus and waited for the pupils to follow. **I** _____ [17] put on

their boots and quietly left the bus … all except Claudia and Amelia.

'**They** _____ [18] are such an idiot! I'll _____ [19] think **he** _____ [20]

threw **her** _____ [21]', whispered Claudia angrily.

'Oh, **we**'m _____ [22] so sorry Claudia!' squealed Amelia in a fit of giggles. '**He** _____ [23]

didn't realise **you** _____ [24] was **ours** _____ [25].' 'Claudia this is **mine**

_____, [26] **you** _____ [27] presume', boomed Mr Posset, holding up the boot

triumphantly.

Parts of speech
Pronouns

Focus

Relative pronouns including **who** and **whom**

Definition

- A **relative pronoun** comes before the clause that describes the noun or pronoun to which it refers.

  Example:

  *The artist **who** illustrated comic books was very talented.*

  who (the relative pronoun) comes before **illustrated comic books** (the relative clause) which describes the **artist** (the noun to which it refers)

Explanation

- It is important for pupils to know the correct relative pronouns to use in the context of a particular sentence so their grammar, in speech and in writing, is accurate.

- The words **who**, **which**, **that, whose, when** and **where** are only relative pronouns within the context of the sentence.

  Example:

  *The composer **who** wrote symphonies was a talented musician.* (relative pronoun)

  ***Who** is the composer of this symphony?* (interrogative pronoun)

- The following examples demonstrate how each relative pronoun can be used.

  *The tent **that** collapsed in the storm was severely damaged.*

  *I cleared the gutters **which** were full of leaves.*

  *The donkey **whose** call was loud was the village mascot.*

  *The days **when** we played cricket will be remembered.*

  *The stream **where** I used to fish is now polluted.*

  *The farmer **who** grew wheat milled his own flour.*

  *This is the singer **whom** we all want to hear.*

Note 1: The choice of **that** or **which** is intuitive. The general rule is to try **that** first but if it doesn't sound right, use **which**.

It may be appropriate to explain to pupils that **that** tends to be used when speaking about general things and **which** for more specific things.

Example:

*Trees **that** lose their leaves in autumn are called deciduous.*

*These trees, **which** lose their leaves in autumn, are called deciduous.*

Note 2: The relative pronouns **who** and **whom** are used when referring to people.

- **Who** is used when that person is doing the action of a verb. (the subject)

- **Whom** is used when the action of the verb is done to that person. (the object)

  Example:

  *The sea captain, **who** had sailed the high seas, retired to a quiet fishing village.*

  – *The sea captain had sailed the high seas and so **who** is used because **the sea captain** is the subject of the verb, **had sailed**.*

  *The sea captain, **whom** the entire crew respected, retired to a quiet fishing village.*

  – *The sea captain is respected by his crew and so **whom** is used because **the sea captain** is the object of the verb, **respected**.*

Worksheet information

- Revise the use of all the relative pronouns, paying particular attention to Note 1 and Note 2 above.

- The verbs in Questions 1 and 2 have been highlighted to assist the pupils to identify the subject of each.

Ideas for further practice

- Pupils write a description of a holiday destination for a travel brochure and present it as a cloze procedure, removing any relative pronouns. They can be distributed for the class to complete.

- Demonstrate examples of sentences using **who** and **whom** with pupils showing the action and having the action done to them.

Answers

1. (a) who   (b) whom   (c) who
   (d) whom   (e) who   (f) whom

2. (a) who   (b) whom   (c) whose
   (d) who   (e) whom   (f) whose

3. 1. where   2. whose   3. that
   4. who   5. whom   6. where
   7. when   8. which

Relative pronouns

A **relative pronoun** starts with a clause that describes a noun or pronoun.
The relative pronouns **who** and **whom** are used when referring to people.

1. Choose *who* or *whom* for each sentence. The verbs are in italics.

   (a) The singer _____ *performed* for royalty received much publicity.

   (b) The singer _____ the press *had interviewed*, had performed for royalty.

   (c) The swimmer _____ *had qualified* to swim for her country was ecstatic.

   (d) The swimmer _____ the qualifying board *had chosen,* was ecstatic.

   (e) The scientist _____ *discovered* a cure was given the prestigious award.

   (f) The scientist to _____ the prestigious award *was given*, had discovered a cure.

2. Choose *who, whom* or *whose* for each sentence. The verbs are in italics.

   (a) The pupil _____ *practised* regularly became a fine musician.

   (b) The girl _____ we *left out* of the team was a better swimmer than any of us.

   (c) The boy _____ laces *were* undone tripped over as he ran down the stairs.

   (d) The child _____ *lost* her pet was very sad.

   (e) The teacher _____ we all *loved* left school today.

   (f) The parents _____ children *were* in trouble at school felt embarrassed.

3. Choose the correct relative pronoun for each of the gaps in the text. (One is used twice.)

who	where	whom	that	which	whose	when

South America is the place _____ [1] all intrepid explorers _____ [2]

ideal holiday is to 'get out of the square', can go in search of a dream.

Each day will bring new adventures _____ [3] will stimulate the senses. From

snorkelling and diving in the Galapagos Islands to cycling down a volcano in Ecuador,

the opportunities are endless.

Anyone _____ [4] has ever dreamed of a spectacular hiking holiday

will be enthralled by the Inca Trail to Machu Picchu high in the Peruvian Andes.

The local people with _____ [5] you can stay throughout your

trip will welcome you into their villages _____ [6] you will

experience the sights, sounds and tastes of their culture.

A trip to South America will leave you with the memory of a

time _____ [7] you left your comfort zone and were

rewarded with an experience _____ [8] you will never forget.

Parts of speech
Conjunctions

Focus

Conjunctions

Definitions

- **Conjunctions** are joining words which can be used to connect words, phrases, clauses or sentences.

  Example:

  salt **and** pepper

  a fast car **but** difficult to control

  Since I have no money, I can't go to the circus.

- **Correlative conjunctions** are conjunctions used in pairs to show the relationship between ideas expressed in different parts of a sentence.

  Example:

  I would **rather** go swimming **than** go to the library.

Explanation

- Using conjunctions enables a writer to build and combine ideas and cut out needless repetition.

  Conjunctions can join:

  – one adjective with another, for example:

  The girl was hot **and** tired.

  – one sentence with another, for example:

  It was raining **so** I took an umbrella.

  Conjunctions can be placed between two clauses or at the beginning of a sentence. The position of the conjunction helps the reader to know which part of the sentence is the focus.

  Example:

  '**If** you climb on top of the monkey bars, you will fall.'
  (Focus is on the cause)

  '**You will fall** if you climb on top of the monkey bars.'
  (Focus is on the consequence)

Worksheet information

- To remind pupils of words that can be used as conjunctions, ask each pupil to write one on the board.

  Example:

  and, but, because, although, for, while

- Before pupils begin Questions 2 and 3, the teacher may wish to model extending sentences and making sentences more interesting by adding conjunctions.

Ideas for further practice

- Pupils write a speech on something they feel strongly about. Include correlative conjunctions.

- View texts such as newspaper, magazine and Internet articles to find conjunctions which are compound words. Make a list.

  Example:

  furthermore, nevertheless, meanwhile, whenever

Answers

1. (a) and (b) Bold text = correlative conjunction
   Underlined text = conjunction

   Will <u>and</u> James ran towards the smoking wreck. <u>Although</u> bleeding quite heavily, the pilot was able to climb out of the plane. **No sooner** had he reached the ground, **than** he collapsed. The boys ran towards the pilot <u>then</u> they froze, <u>as</u> **neither** had first aid training **nor** the faintest idea what to do.

   '**Either** you **or** I will have to go <u>and</u> get help', announced James.

   Will volunteered, <u>as</u> he was **both** a fast runner **and** fit. He sprinted to the nearest phone box <u>which</u> he soon discovered to be out of order. <u>While</u> he looked up <u>and</u> down the road for another phone box, a police car drove past. Will didn't know **whether** to laugh **or** cry <u>as</u> he frantically waved down the car.

2.–3. Answers will vary

Conjunctions

A **conjunction** is a joining word which can be used to join words, phrases, clauses and sentences.

Did you know some conjunctions come in pairs? They are called correlative conjunctions.

Example: '**Either** you **or** I will have to change seats.'   (either ... or)

'She is **neither** rich **nor** famous.'   (neither ... nor)

'Your work is **both** neat **and** accurate.'   (both ... and)

No sooner had the clock struck **than** he left.   (no sooner ... than)

Decide **whether** to go **or** stay.   (whether ... or)

Reminder
Conjunctions can start a sentence.

1. **Read the text.**

   (a)   Circle the five pairs of correlative conjunctions.

   (b)   Underline the 10 other conjunctions found in the text.

   > Will and James ran towards the smoking wreck. Although bleeding quite heavily, the pilot was able to climb out of the plane. No sooner had he reached the ground than he collapsed. The boys ran towards the pilot then they froze, as neither had first aid training nor the faintest idea what to do.
   >
   > 'Either you or I will have to go and get help', announced James.
   >
   > Will volunteered, as he was both a fast runner and fit. He sprinted to the nearest phone box which he discovered was out of order. While he looked up and down the road for another phone box, a police car drove past. Will didn't know whether to laugh or cry as he frantically waved down the car.

2. **Write your own sentences containing correlative conjunctions.**

   (a)   I will either _____ or _____ .

   (b)   I like neither _____ nor _____ .

   (c)   Her cooking is not only _____ but _____ .

   (d)   Your dancing is both _____ and _____ .

3. **Extend the sentence using these conjunctions:**   *while   since   if   so*

   For example: Dad lit the fire.

   • While Mum served the soup, Dad lit the fire.   • Since Dad lit the fire, it had started to snow.

   • If Dad lit the fire, we could toast marshmallows.   • Dad lit the fire so we could warm up.

   (a)   Ellie washed the dog.

   • _____

   • _____

   • _____

   • _____

   (b)   On the back of this sheet, make the following sentences more interesting by adding conjunctions and joining them. **Challenge: try adding a correlative conjunction!**

   • The cat sat on the mat.   • It was cold outside.   • Talia walked into the classroom.

Parts of speech
Determiners

Focus

Articles: the (definite), a/an (indefinite)

Possessives: my, your, his, her, its, our, their

Demonstratives: this, that (singular), these, those (plural)

Definitions

- A **determiner** is a word usually used before a noun that determines how definite it is.

  Example:

  > **Our** homework was placed on **that** table with **some** books because **the** teacher wanted us to take **a** book home **each** night.

- **Articles** are a subclass of determiners.

  Example:

  > **a** book (meaning any book), **the** book (meaning a particular book)

- A **possessive determiner** is a word which identifies who the thing belongs to.

  Example:

  > Mary sold **her** book at the fete.

- A **demonstrative** determiner signals whether the associated noun is **near** (*this, these*) or **far away** (*that, those*) from the writer or speaker.

  Note: In traditional grammar, some words used as what are now called **determiners** in functional grammar are referred to as **adjectives**; e.g. *first, seven* or as **possessive pronouns**; e.g. *our, your*.

Explanation

- Determiners are useful for making information more precise for the reader or listener.

- The definite article **the** is used to refer to a particular thing or things and when referring to specific, one-of-a-kind things.

  Example:

  > **the** Nile River, **the** book (meaning a particular book)

- Indefinite articles such as **a** and **an** are used to refer to any thing. The noun following an indefinite article is non-specific.

  Example:

  > **a** boat (meaning any boat) or **an** umbrella (meaning any umbrella)

- Articles can indicate a significant difference in meaning.

  Example:

  > **a** house (any house) and **the** house (a particular house)

- The indefinite article **a** precedes a noun that begins with a consonant sound.

  Example:

  > **a** yacht, **a** boat, **a** dog, **a** unicycle

- The indefinite article **an** precedes a noun that begins with a vowel sound.

  Example:

  > **an** apple, **an** ice-cream, **an** umbrella, **an** hour

- **Possessive determiners** are always used before the noun to say who the noun belongs to. They can be used in first, second or third person form as well as in singular or plural. Refer to the table below to see which **possessive determiners** are used in each situation.

	Person	Determiner	Pronouns
Singular	1st	my	I, me, mine
	2nd	your	you, yours
	3rd	his	he, him, his
		her	she, her, hers
		its	it, its
Plural	1st	our	we, us, ours
	2nd	your	you, yours
	3rd	their	they, them, theirs

- **Demonstratives** generally indicate the proximity of the noun to the writer or speaker. **This** (singular) and **these** (plural) suggest the noun is close by, while **that** (singular) and **those** (plural) suggest the noun is far away or out of reach.

Worksheet information

- Short explanations of each type of determiner have been given to the pupils to further develop their knowledge and understanding.

Ideas for further practice

- Pupils write their own sentences highlighting the determiner used and give a brief explanation of the role of the determiner in the sentence.

Answers

1. (a) The, a   (b) The
   (c) An   (d) The, an   (e) the

2. (a) those (far)   (b) this (near)
   (c) these (near)   (d) That (far)
   (e) these (near)   (f) those (far)

3. (a) his, her   (b) its
   (c) our   (d) your
   (e) Their, my

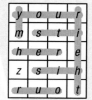

Determiners – 1

A **determiner** is usually used before a noun to determine how definite it is.

For example: **Our** homework was placed on **that** table with **some** books because **the** teacher wanted us to take **a** book home **each** night.

1. Use an article in each blank space to complete these sentences.

   An **article** is a type of determiner.

   The is a definite article. When it is used, we know the noun is a specific thing.

   A or **an** are indefinite articles. When either one is used, we know the noun is not specific.

   (a) _____ people next door own _____ dog which is noisy at night.

   (b) _____ house at number 22 is quite run down.

   (c) _____ echidna is an animal found only in Australia.

   (d) _____ boys rode for _____ hour before they became tired.

   (e) If _____ cat annoys you, just let me know.

2. Underline the demonstrative determiner in each of these sentences. Identify whether the noun is near to the writer or far from the writer.

   A *demonstrative determiner* is a word used before singular or plural nouns to show how far from or near to the writer or speaker the noun is.

   (a) Please ask those boys to come over here. .... | near | far |

   (b) I am certain *this* book belongs to you. .... | near | far |

   (c) Are you sure *these* socks are a pair? .... | near | far |

   (d) *That* girl looks lonely, maybe you could play with her. .... | near | far |

   (e) I like the idea of having *these* fish in our tank. .... | near | far |

   (f) I think *those* fish look beautiful swimming among the reef. .... | near | far |

3. Hidden in the word search are seven possessive determiners. Find them and use them to complete the sentences.

   A *possessive determiner* is a word used before a noun to tell who the noun belongs to.

y	o	u	r
m	s	t	i
h	e	r	e
z	s	i	h
r	u	o	t

   (a) Since it was _____ sister who fell off _____ bike, Carl was very concerned.

   (b) The cat always licks _____ paws after eating dinner.

   (c) We think the flowers we planted in _____ garden look beautiful.

   (d) Make sure you don't lose _____ money.

   (e) _____ mum wasn't very well, so _____ mum looked after the three children.

Parts of speech

Determiners

Focus

Determiners

Distributives: either, neither, each, every

Interrogatives: which, what, whose

Quantifiers: all, both, most, some, any, no, few, fewer, much, more, less, least, a little, a lot of, a great deal of

Definitions

- A **determiner** is a word usually used before a noun that determines how definite it is.

  Example:

  > **Our** homework was placed on **that** table with **some** books because **the** teacher wanted us to take **a** book home **each** night.

- A **distributive** is a type of determiner which tells how something is distributed, shared or divided.

  Example:

  > I think **every** person is special.

- An **interrogative** is a type of determiner used before a noun to form a question.

  Example:

  > **Whose** book is that?

- A **quantifier** is a type of determiner which tells how many things or people without giving a precise number.

  Example:

  > There are **a lot of** lollies in the jar.

Note: In traditional grammar, some words used as what are now called **determiners** in functional grammar, were referred to as **adjectives**; e.g. first, seven or **possessive pronouns**; e.g. my, your.

Explanation

- Determiners are useful for making information more precise for the reader or listener.
- Distributive determiners are usually used before the noun.
- **Each** and **every** have similar meanings and it's often possible to use either of them.

  Each can mean everyone separately or one by one and can be used for one of two things. It can be followed by 'of' and can be used in front of a verb.

  Every can mean 'each' and sometimes 'all'. It cannot be used for two things or after 'of'. It can be used to say 'how often'.

- **Either** and **neither** refer to one or none of two things.
- Verbs used after **each**, **every**, **either** and **neither** are singular as are any related possessive determiners.

  Example:

  > Each of the boys **eats his** dinner.
  >
  > Every person **has** worn **his** or **her** hat.
  >
  > Either sports car **appeals** to **its** drivers.
  >
  > Neither woman **wants to drive** her car.

- 'Which', 'what' and 'whose' are also known as 'question words' because they are used to create a question. Ensure these words are placed before the noun they relate to.
- **Quantifiers** are placed before the noun.
- Some **quantifiers** are used only with plural nouns: **few**, **a few**, **fewer**, **many**. Others can be used with singular or plural nouns: **some**, **a lot of**, **lots of**, **more**, **most**, **plenty of**. Other quantifiers can only be used with singular nouns: **little**, **a little**, **much**, **less**.

Worksheet information

- Short explanations of each type of determiner have been given to further develop pupils' knowledge and understanding.
- Explain that only keywords in some determiners are needed in the crossword.

Ideas for further practice

- Create mobiles with the determiner type at the top of the mobile, then the words which belong within the category hanging below.

  Example:

  > Interrogatives—what, which, whose.

Answers

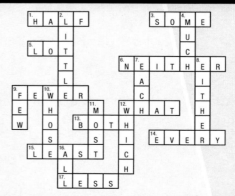

Determiners - 2

A *determiner* is usually used before a noun to determine how definite it is.
For example: *Our* homework was placed on *that* table with *some* books because *the* teacher wanted us to take *a* book home *each* night.

Read the sentences. Only underline the particular determiner stated in the heading at the top of the section. Use the key underlined words to solve the crossword puzzle.

Quantifiers

These determiners tell us the quantity of the noun without giving a precise number.

1A I could only eat half the pie before I felt sick.

2D Mum uses a little salt in the cooking.

3A It is important to eat some fruit on a daily basis.

4D I like to drink as much water as I can.

5A I like to eat a lot of grapes in the summer.

9A My younger brother seems to do fewer chores around the house than I do.

9D We have a few pets to love and look after.

11D The bush with the most flowers always looks stunning.

13A It is important to cover both wounds carefully to help them heal.

15A The plants that require the least water are found in the desert.

16D I ate all the ice-cream without asking.

17A The less work you do, the less likely you are to succeed.

Interrogatives

These determiners are used to create a question.

10D Whose drink bottle has been left on the floor?

12A What time does the party start?

12D Which topping would you like on your pancakes?

Distributives

These determiners tell us how the noun is shared or divided.

6A Neither boy wanted to share his new toy.

7D It is expected that each child will complete the set tasks by the due date.

8D I think either top will look nice with that skirt.

14A If every person gave more consideration to conserving energy, our environment would be better off.

Parts of speech
Prepositions

Focus

Prepositions and adverbs

Definition

- **Prepositions** are words used to show the relationship between nouns and/or pronouns or noun phrases in the same sentence.
  Example:
  *'The Jones's are moving **from** Cork **to** Dublin **in** April **for** work.'*

Explanation

- The word 'preposition' combines the prefix 'pre' (meaning 'before' or 'in front of') and the word 'position'. As such, prepositions are words that are 'positioned in front' of nouns or other words that functions as nouns (such as pronouns, verbal nouns or noun phrases).
- Prepositions indicate a connection between things mentioned in a sentence, such as between a person and where she/he is going.
  Example:
  *Jill moved **towards** the table.*
  Prepositions can refer to manner.
  Example:
  *He came to work **by** bus.*
  Prepositions can refer to time.
  Example:
  *School starts **at** 9 am.*
  Prepositions can refer to place.
  Example:
  *He left his shoes **at** the park.*
  Prepositions can refer to position.
  Example:
  *The cat lay **under** the table.*
  Prepositions can refer to direction.
  Example:
  *It ran **between** the buildings.*
  Prepositions can have some special uses.
  Example:
  comparison, to tell why, to support or oppose something

Some prepositions are formed by combining multiple words, such as 'in front of', 'on top of' and 'prior to'.

- Prepositions often introduce phrases that add more information to the noun or verb. These phrases are called **prepositional phrases** and start with a preposition and end with a noun or noun equivalent, called the 'object' of the preposition. Words that modify the object are part of the phrase.
  Example:
  *The girl (subject), though tall, was still shorter **than** (preposition) her younger brother' (object). (The prepositional phrase is underlined.)*
- As a rule, prepositions do not come before verbs.
- A former 'rule' was that prepositions should never end a sentence. This was because the traditional rules of English grammar were taken from Latin, and in Latin it is not possible to end a sentence with a preposition. This rule no longer applies; for example, it is commonly accepted as correct to say:
  *'Have you found the shoes you were looking **for**?'*
  rather than the old English:
  *'Have you found the shoes **for** which you were looking?'*
- Prepositions are frequently used in speech and add meaning and detail. They also help to distinguish between the object and the subject in a sentence. Commonly used prepositions include: ***about, above, across, after, against, around, at, before, behind, beneath, beside, between, beyond, by, for, from, in, inside, near, off, on, out, over, through, to, toward, under, until, upon*** and ***with***. Bear in mind that these words are not always prepositions; sometimes they function as conjunctions or adverbs.

Example:
*In 'Mia decided to stay **inside**', 'inside' has no object, and so is an adverb.*

Worksheet information

- Read the explanation with pupils and clarify before they find the prepositions.
- Pupils should choose some suitable prepositions in Question 2 then use or change them to complete the crossword.
- Read the explanation and revise adverbs, (see pages 18–21) before pupils complete Question 3.

Further practice

- Make a list of preposition pairs, such as complain + about, concerned + about, bored + with, interested + in. Give one card to each pupil and give them a certain time period (e.g. two minutes) to find the correct matching card.
  Example:
  the pupil with 'pounce' must find the pupil with 'upon'
- Pupils could underline prepositions in newspaper articles and discuss the prepositions they found.

Answers

1. with, about, to, about, to, By, of, for, with, for, Before, to, for, after

2.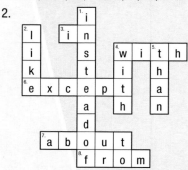

3. preposition
   adverb
   preposition
   adverb

Prepositions

Prepositions show the connection between nouns, pronouns and noun phrases and are usually placed in the front of them in sentences.

They can refer to place (*at* the table), time (*before* lunch) and movement (*towards* the river).

1. Underline the prepositions.

> Mrs Smith got really angry with Class Six yesterday. The class complained about the work they had to do, paid no attention to her instructions and didn't think about their answers to her questions. By morning break, she said she'd had enough **of** the class and set lines for everyone to write. 'What's the matter with you today?' she asked. 'What's the reason **for** this terrible behaviour?' Before lunch, some of the pupils apologised to her **for** their behaviour. Things were much better after that.

2. Complete the crossword using prepositions.

   Across

   3. Jacob wasn't interested ___ cars.

   4. What's wrong ___ Luke today?

   6. I'll eat anything ___ broccoli!

   7. What did Lee tell you ___ his hobby?

   8. My answers are totally different ___ yours.

   Down

   1. We could go to the park ___ watching TV.

   2. Josh is tall ___ his mum.

   4. Mr Kitcher was really pleased ___ my work!

   5. My little brother is taller ___ me!

Some words often used as prepositions can be used as adverbs.
They are likely to be adverbs if followed by a verb or no words.
For example:

> A submarine can dive **below** the surface. (preposition)
> Their equipment detected the submarine **below**. (adverb)

---

3. Read the sentences and decide if the underlined words are prepositions or adverbs.

   (a) My grandfather migrated <u>from</u> China when he was a young man. _____

   (b) He became a market gardener because he enjoyed working <u>outside</u>. _____

   (c) My father worked <u>with</u> him when he was old enough. _____

   (d) His sister preferred to stay <u>inside</u> and help her mother cook. _____

Understanding and choosing words
Homographs

Focus

Homographs

Definition

- **Homographs** are words that are spelt the same but have different meanings.

  Example:

  mine – *a large hole dug to extract minerals*

  mine – *a type of bomb*

  (Note: There are more than these two meanings.)

  Sometimes homographs are pronounced differently.

  Example:

  minute *(emphasis on first syllable)* – *sixty seconds*

  minute *(emphasis on second syllable)* – *extremely small*

Explanation

- Recognising and using different homographs develops and enriches pupils' vocabulary. They learn to understand the meaning of words and the way they work in print.

Worksheet information

- As an introduction, give two quiz questions to the pupils to demonstrate two different meanings for the same word.

  For example;

  Question 1: This homograph is a noun. What name do we give for a tool that smooths wood?

  Question 2: This homograph is also a noun. What word means a machine with wings that can fly? Ask them to guess the word and discuss the different meanings. Pupils may suggest other meanings for 'plane' such as to lift partly out of water when going at high speed, like a speed boat.

- Complete Question 1 on the worksheet and discuss the pupils' answers.

- In Question 2, pupils are provided with a text that contains several homographs. The most obvious homographs are in bold print. Pupils choose eight to write in any order next to each bullet point, giving a definition to explain how the word is used in the text and another meaning for the word. Dictionaries could be used to assist. Again, discuss pupils' answers as a class as there are more than two meanings for many words.

- The word 'object' in Question 3 is an example of a

homograph that has different pronunciations. Discuss this with the pupils before they complete the activity. Discuss their answers.

Ideas for further practice

- This activity could be done in pairs. Pupils create sentences using a homograph twice in the same sentence, with each homograph showing a different meaning; e.g. We will not be able to give my **dear** old Grandad that recliner chair for his birthday as it is too **dear**.

- Pupils identify homographs that have different pronunciations and compile a class reference chart.

  Example:

  wind *(rhymes with* **tinned***)* and **wind** *(rhymes with* **fined***)*

  present *(emphasis on first syllable)* and **present** *(emphasis on second syllable)*

Answers

1. Possible answers. Sentences that explain:

   – a small piece of ground (noun)

   – a secret scheme (noun)

   – to mark out a route (verb)

   – to secretly plan something (verb)

2. Teacher check. Possible answers for homographs used in the text:

   last: eventually
   date: relating to the day on a calendar
   left: past tense of the verb 'to leave'
   launch: to send into the water
   squash: crush
   deck: the 'floor' of a boat
   stable: firm and steady
   cape: a section of land that juts out into the ocean
   flounder: a type of fish
   firm: definite, unchanging
   refuse: (emphasis on second syllable) the opposite of 'accept'
   deal: an agreement

3. (a) object: (emphasis on first syllable) something that can be seen and felt

   (b) object: (emphasis on second syllable) to argue against

Homographs

Homographs are words spelt the same that have more than one meaning.

1. Write three more sentences that show other meanings for the word 'plot'.

   (a) I enjoyed reading that novel as the **plot** had many twists and turns.

   (b) _____

   (c) _____

   (d) _____

2. Read the text below. The words in bold print are homographs. Choose eight to list below. Write a definition for each word that matches its meaning in the text and then another meaning underneath.

> At **last**! The **date** we had made for a fishing trip with my uncle and cousins had finally arrived. We **left** at dawn for the marina to **launch** the boat. It was a bit of a **squash** on **deck** as we all wanted to be up there to smell the salty breeze. The boat was **stable** and the trip to the secluded bay around the **cape** did not take long. Uncle Matt headed towards the shallower waters first so we could try to catch some **flounder**. He made a **firm** decision to **refuse** to leave until one of us had caught a fish. We thought that would be an easy **deal** to keep—or so we hoped!

_____ : • _____

                          • _____

_____ : • _____

                          • _____

_____ : • _____

                          • _____

_____ : • _____

                          • _____

_____ : • _____

                          • _____

_____ : • _____

                          • _____

_____ : • _____

                          • _____

_____ : • _____

                          • _____

3. The word 'object' can be pronounced in two ways. Give a definition for each.

   (a) object (emphasis on first syllable) _____

   (b) object (emphasis on second syllable) _____

Understanding and choosing words

Homophones

Focus

Homophones

Definition

- **Homophones** are words that sound the same but are spelt differently and have different meanings.
  Example:

  > ***draught*** – *a current of air;*
  >
  > ***draft*** – *a first or preliminary form of any writing*

Explanation

- The word 'homo**phone**' means 'same **sound**'. Homo**nyms** ('same **name**') include both homophones and homo**graphs** ('same **writing**').

- Identifying different homophones and recognising how to spell them helps pupils to communicate more clearly in written form. Investigating homophones also helps to develop and enrich pupils' vocabulary. They learn to understand the meaning of words and the way they work in print.

- Correct spelling is essential when using homophones. No spelling rules exist for spelling pairs or groups of homophones to help pupils remember them.

Worksheet information

- Possible incorrect homophones have been included in the text. Pupils should read through the text to get the sense of the text before going back to highlight the incorrect words used.

- Ask pupils to read the definition and explain it in reference to the examples in the text. They can then write the correct words above.

- Pupils should be able to complete Question 2 with minimal assistance.

Ideas for further practice

- Make up mnemonics such as clever sentences or rhymes to help remember the difference in spelling and meaning of groups of homophones.

- Homophones make eye-catching names for shops etc. For example, 'Fish Plaice' (Fish and chip shop), 'Sew Fantastic' (sewing and material shop), 'Home Suite Home' or 'Suite Dreams' (furniture shop), and 'Meat at the Corner' (butcher shop). Use a local phone book to locate others to share with the class.

Answers

1. This **morning**, while I **ate** my **cereal**, I listened to the **weather** report. It usually **pours** with rain when I **wear** my best clothes. I made a quick **check** of my backpack and made **sure** that I had on the correct shoes to **complement** my outfit and then I was on my **way**. Today we are going to **practise** giving speeches in the **council** chambers as part of our study of democracy. We had to get to school early and go **straight** to the local **council** building. Unfortunately, the bus driver drove very fast and I wondered if he got his driving **licence** out of a **cereal** box.

2. (a)

		¹C	H	E	Q	U	E		
		²B	O	U	G	H			
				³M	E	D	D	L	E
	⁴S	T	O	R	Y				
⁵P	R	I	N	C	I	P	A	L	
		⁶R	I	G	H	T			
	⁷T	H	R	O	U	G	H		
			⁸K	N	I	G	H	T	
		⁹S	E	I	Z	E			
¹⁰H	O	A	R	S	E				

(b) The mystery word is *homophones*.

(c) cheque/check, bough/bow, meddle/medal, storey/story, principle/principal, right/write/rite, through/threw, knight/night, seize/seas/sees, hoarse/horse

Homophones

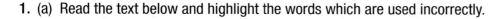

Homophones are words that sound the same but are spelt differently and have different meanings. Correct spelling is very important.

1. (a) Read the text below and highlight the words which are used incorrectly.

> This mourning, while I eight my serial, I listened to the whether report. It usually paws with rain when I where my best clothes. I made a quick cheque of my backpack and made shore that I had on the correct shoes to compliment my outfit and then I was on my weigh.
>
> Today we are going to practice giving speeches in the counsel chambers as part of our study of democracy. We had to get to school early and go strait to the local counsel building. Unfortunately, the bus driver drove very fast and I wondered if he got his driving license out of a serial box.

(b) Write the correct homophone above each highlighted word.

2. (a) Use the clues to complete the word puzzle.

Clues

1. money order paid by a bank *(noun)*
2. branch of a tree *(noun)*
3. to interfere with something that doesn't concern you *(verb)*
4. a tale *(noun)*
5. head of a school or college *(noun)*
6. correct *(adjective)*
7. in one end and out the other *(preposition)*
8. a medieval nobleman who pledged to serve the king *(noun)*
9. to take hold suddenly *(verb)*
10. rough or croaky voice *(adjective)*

(b) Identify the word down the centre. _____

(c) Write a homophone for each word in the word puzzle.

1.	2.	3.
4.	5.	6.
7.	8.	9.
10.		

Understanding and choosing words
Eponyms

Eponyms

Definition

- **Eponyms** are words derived from a person's name or the name of a place.

  Example:

  *The word **saxophone** comes from Adolphe Sax, a Belgium musical-instrument maker.*

  *The **Venn** diagram is named after John Venn, an English mathematician and logician.*

Explanation

- Eponyms come from the name of a real, fictitious or mythical character, person or a place. Most are derived from the surnames of people. There are a great many eponyms used in the English language, helping to make it a rich and diverse language.

- Understanding where words originate gives pupils a greater appreciation of the complexity of the English language and expands their vocabulary. It also gives them a basis for comparing and comprehending other words.

Worksheet information

- Pupils should be able to complete the worksheet with minimal assistance. A good dictionary will supply many of the answers for Question 2. Eighteen eponyms are listed in the answers on this page.

Ideas for further practice

- Write a nonsense text using as many eponyms as possible. These can be eponyms belonging to a particular category such as food.

  Example,

  pavlova, peach Melba

- Write clues for a crossword puzzle using eponyms, including the derivation of each eponym.

- Pupils create an eponym based on themselves, their characteristics or some of their favourite sayings.

Answers

1.

V	T	M	V	L	A	R	O	L	F
M	H	T	I	R	O	G	L	A	U
W	E	U	B	B	Z	A	E	R	V
Q	U	S	L	E	B	E	O	A	V
K	W	U	M	L	T	T	C	V
Z	R	Y	N	E	T	J	A	H	D
B	X	N	S	O	R	U	R	N	F
T	A	E	M	U	G	I	D	I	Y
C	I	A	L	J	S	Z	S	D	F
D	N	L	A	D	N	A	V	E	T

2. **Thursdays** – *Thor*, Norse god of thunder

   Fridays – *Frig (or Frigga)*, Norse god of married love

   galvanise – *Luigi Galvani*, Italian physiologist

   groggy – *Old Grog*, nickname of Sir Edward Vernon, British admiral

   panic – *Pan*, Greek god of the woods, shepherds and flocks

   hooligan – almost certainly from the Houlihan family in the 1890s

   tantalise – *Tantalis*, mythical king of Phrygia

   zany – *Zanni*, an Italian traditional masked clown

   tomfoolery – a fictional English fool, Thom Foole

   bobby – *Sir Robert Peel*, founder of the London Police Force

   cretin – *crestin*, name of a French dialect

   slave – *Sclavus*, Medieval Latin for 'Slav' (Slavic people of central Europe)

   biro™ – Hungarian inventor, *László Jozsef Biró*

   boycott – Irish land agent, *Charles C Boycott*

   Mount Everest – English surveyor-general of India, *Sir George Everest*

   Eiffel Tower – French engineer, *Alexandre Gustave Eiffel*

   the **Elgin Marbles** – *Thomas Bruce*, 7th Earl of Elgin, British Ambassador

   Davis Cup – *Dwight Filley Davis*, American sportsman

Eponyms

An *eponym* is a word that comes from a person's name or the name of a place.

1. Use the clues to find and write the eponyms in the word search.

   (a) someone who deliberately destroys property (from the Vandals, who overran Gaul, Spain, North Africa and Rome in the fifth century)

   _____

   (b) the setting out of a mathematical problem in a certain way (from al-Khwarizmi, an Arab mathematician)

   _____

   (c) a cushioned footstool or seat (from Othman, sultan of Turkey)

   _____

   (d) a group of arthropods including spiders, scorpions, mites etc. (from Arachne, a girl turned into a spider by Athena)

   _____

   (e) to completely hold the attention of (from Franz Anton Mesmer, Austrian physician and hypnotist)

   _____

   (f) an advertisement on a book (from an illustration of a fictional character, Miss Belinda Blurb)

   _____

   (g) a garment (from Jules Léotard, French acrobat)

   _____

   (h) human-flesh eater (from Canibales, name given to a group of Caribbean Indian people)

   _____

   (i) oil (from Rudolf Diesel, German mechanical engineer)

   _____

   (j) plants (from Flora, Roman goddess of flowers, youth and spring)

   _____

V	T	M	V	L	A	R	O	L	F
M	H	T	I	R	O	G	L	A	U
W	E	U	B	B	Z	A	E	R	V
Q	U	S	L	E	B	E	O	A	V
K	W	U	M	I	L	T	T	C	V
Z	R	Y	N	E	T	J	A	H	D
B	X	N	S	O	R	U	R	N	F
T	A	E	M	U	G	I	D	I	Y
C	I	A	L	J	S	Z	S	D	F
D	N	L	A	D	N	A	V	E	T

2. (a) Read the nonsense text and circle at least twelve eponyms. Use a dictionary, the library, Internet or other sources to find where these words came from.

   (b) Record your findings and share them with the class.

   Thursdays and Fridays are my favourite days of the week. Those days galvanise me into action for some reason and I don't feel groggy at all and I don't panic. I don't actually act like a hooligan but I am poised and ready. Those days tantalise me with the weekend that is coming. By Saturday, I act a bit zany, and I am ready for a bit of tomfoolery. It's lucky there is not a bobby in sight or I would have to stop acting like a cretin. But by Monday I am a slave to the black biro™ again as I sit at my desk adding numbers and writing reports. One day, I'll boycott the work place and travel the world visiting places like Mount Everest, the Eiffel Tower, the Elgin Marbles or places where the Davis Cup is held.

Understanding and choosing words

Euphemisms

Focus

Euphemisms

Definition

- A **euphemism** is a word or expression substituted for another that might cause offense.

  Example,

  'pre-loved'/'pre-owned' for 'used' or 'secondhand'

  'rest room' for 'toilet'

Explanation

- Some topics which are personal or sensitive are often spoken of in a more pleasant manner. Euphemisms can become part of everyday language. Like colloquial language, some euphemisms appear in dictionaries after they become widely accepted. Euphemisms accepted and easily understood in one country, region or town may not be accepted or understood in another.

Worksheet information

- Pupils read the explanation and the text. They should be able to work out the meaning of the euphemisms from contextual information and answer Question 2.
- Encourage creativity in Question 3.

Ideas for further practice

- In small groups, discuss answers to Question 3 and decide which answers are appropriate and which are not. Give reasons for answers and try to persuade others that the euphemism is an appropriate one.
- Identify and explain euphemisms found while reading texts such as class readers or library books and home novels.
- Draw caricatures which illustrate euphemisms and try to guess what they are.

Answers

1. When I heard that Gran had **the big C**, I was so distressed that I fled to the **rest room** and **lost my lunch**. I had to wipe my face with wet **bathroom tissue**. I know at nearly ninety, Gran is considered to be a **mature** lady, but, to me, she will always be **young at heart** and we just expect that she will always be there. I could not consider her **passing away**. In our family, we call her **chronologically advantaged**. Even when we visit and she **has a power nap** while we are there, no-one minds, because that's just Gran! We rarely **have words** even when I am **between jobs** and just a little **financially embarrassed**. But Gran is a tough lady so, when I think about it, she will probably live longer than I will!

2. (a) mature, young at heart, chronologically advantaged
   (b) between jobs
   (c) financially embarrassed
   (d) have words
   (e) has a power nap
   (f) the big C
   (g) rest room
   (h) bathroom tissue
   (i) passing away
   (j) lost my lunch

3. Answers will vary but may include the following:
   (a) sanitary landfill
   (b) correctional facility
   (c) pre-owned or pre-loved
   (d) put down/put an end to its suffering/put to sleep
   (e) pass away/pass on/depart this life/pass over/resting in peace
   (f) vertically challenged/vertically disadvantaged
   (g) police action/conflict/hostility

Euphemisms

A **euphemism** is a word or expression substituted for one which could cause offence.

1. Read the text and highlight the euphemisms.

> When I heard that Gran had the big C, I was so distressed that I fled to the rest room and lost my lunch. I had to wipe my face with wet bathroom tissue. I know at nearly ninety, Gran is considered to be a mature lady, but, to me, she will always be young at heart and we just expect that she will always be there. I could not consider her passing away. In our family, we call her chronologically advantaged. Even when we visit and she has a power nap while we are there, no-one minds, because that's just Gran! We rarely have words even when I am between jobs and just a little financially embarrassed. But Gran is a tough lady so, when I think about it, she will probably live longer than I will!

2. For each word or phrase below, write a euphemism from the text. If the word or phrase has more than one euphemism the number of different euphemisms is indicated in brackets.

   (a) old (3) _____

   _____

   _____

   (b) unemployed _____

   (c) poor _____

   (d) argue _____

   (e) falls asleep _____

   (f) cancer _____

   (g) toilet _____

   (h) toilet paper _____

   (i) dying _____

   (j) vomited _____

3. Write an appropriate euphemism for the words below. Your answer may be a well-known euphemism or one of your own creation.

   (a) garbage dump _____

   (b) prison _____

   (c) used or secondhand _____

   (d) euthanise a pet _____

   (e) die _____

   (f) short (not tall) _____

   (g) war _____

Understanding and choosing words

Plurals

Focus

Plurals: adding **s** and **es**

words from other languages

words with the same singular and plural forms

words with no singular form

Definition

* A **plural** is a word used to indicate more than one.

Example:

*three **apples**; three **brushes***

Explanation

* 'Singular' means one. 'Plural' means more than one.
* There are many ways to form the plural of a word.
* To form the plural of most proper nouns, we add **s** or **es**, following the basic pluralisation rules.
* Some words used in English have been 'borrowed' from other languages. Some of these words have been Anglicised and add **s** or **es** to make them plural, while others use the plural of their original language.

Example:

*bacter**ium**—bacter**ia***

* In some instances, context determines how it is made plural.

Example:

***appendix** as traditionally used by physicians becomes **appendixes**,*

***appendix** as traditionally used by a librarian becomes **appendices**.*

* Some words have the same form whether the word is singular or plural.

Example:

salmon

* Some words have no singular form.

Example:

police

Worksheet information

* Pupils may be unfamiliar with some terms used on this worksheet. Ensure a dictionary is available to all pupils and encourage them to use it.
* Discuss each rule with pupils and record similar examples.
* Work with pupils to identify any plural patterns.

Note: Some words have two possible plural forms.

Ideas for further practice

* Collect texts from a variety of sources and highlight the plural words used. Discuss and create a bank of plural words sorted by rules.

Answers

1. We went to the local park with our next door **neighbours**, the **Joneses**. We needed two **leashes** to control our **terriers** so they wouldn't escape into the **bushes** or run onto the busy highway to chase **buses**. Many families were relaxing, eating **sandwiches** out of lunch **boxes**.

2. (a) algae
   (b) apparatus
   (c) bacilli
   (d) bacteria
   (e) data
   (f) genera
   (g) hypotheses
   (h) nuclei
   (i) syntheses

3.

No singular form	Same singular and plural
police, athletics, jeans, pyjamas, scissors, trousers, cattle, binoculars	sheep, aircraft, moose, innings, reindeer, trout, species

Plurals – 1

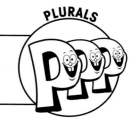

A **plural** is a word used to indicate more than one.
Most nouns are made **plural** by adding **s**.
Nouns ending in **ch**, **sh**, **s**, **x** or **z** add **es** because it's easier to say.

1. Use the plural form of these proper nouns to complete the sentences.

terrier	Jones	box	neighbour	bush	sandwich	leash	bus

We went to the local park with our next door _____, the _____.

We needed two _____ to control our _____ so they wouldn't

escape into the _____ or run onto the busy road to chase _____ .

Many families were relaxing, eating _____ out of lunch _____ .

English has borrowed many words from other languages. This means there are many different ways to make them plural.

2. Write the plural of each word. Underline the part of the word which has changed, if any.

(a) alga _____   nuclei

(b) apparatus _____   bacilli

(c) bacillus _____   hypotheses

(d) bacterium _____   syntheses

(e) datum _____   algae

(f) genus _____   data

(g) hypothesis _____   bacteria

(h) nucleus _____   apparatus

(i) synthesis _____   genera

Some nouns take the same form whether they are singular or plural. Some nouns have no singular form.

3. Sort the nouns and write them in the correct boxes.

police	athletics	species	sheep	jeans	aircraft	moose	pyjamas
scissors	innings	reindeer	trout	trousers	cattle	binoculars	

No singular form	Same singular and plural

Understanding and choosing words

Plurals

Focus

Plurals: words ending with **y**

words ending with **f**

words ending with **o**

Definition

- A **plural** is a word used to indicate more than one.

Example:

*three **apples**; three **brushes***

Explanation

- 'Singular' means one. 'Plural' means more than one.
- There are many ways to form the plural of a word.
- To form the plural of words ending in a vowel and **y**, add **s**.

Example:

*monk**ey** → monkey**s***

- To form the plural of words ending in a consonant and **y**, change **y** to **i** and add **es**.

Example:

*fl**y** → fl**ies***

- To form the plural of some words ending in **f**, add **s**.

Example:

*chie**f** → chie**fs***

- To form the plural of some words ending in **f** or **fe**, change the **f** or **fe** to **v** and add **s**.

Example:

*wi**fe** → wi**ves**, cal**f** → cal**ves***

- To form the plural of some words ending in a consonant and **o**, add **es**.

Example:

*tomat**o** → tomat**oes***

- To form the plural of some words ending in a vowel and **o**, add **s**.

Example:

*radi**o** → radi**os***

Note: There are exceptions to these spelling rules.

Worksheet information:

- Pupils may be unfamiliar with some terms used on this worksheet. Ensure a dictionary is available to all pupils and encourage them to use it. The first spelling given should be selected.
- Discuss each rule and record similar examples.
- Discuss Italian words which end in 'o' and change to 'i' for the plural form.

Example:

bambino → bambini

Ideas for further practice

- Have pupils search for the most unusual or uncommon words they can find to fit under each spelling rule. Create a class dictionary of these words.

Answers

1. (a) **galley** – *a seagoing vessel propelled by oars; galleys*

   adversary – *an unfriendly opponent; adversaries*

   guernsey – *a close fitting vest or shirt; guernseys*

   parody – *a satirical imitation of a serious piece of writing; parodies*

   deity – *a god or goddess; deities*

   tariff – *duties or customs imposed by the government on exports; tariffs*

   waif – *a person without a home or friends; waifs*

   corf – *a small wagon for carrying ore or coal; corves*

   sheaf – *any bundle, cluster or collection; sheaves*

   bilbo – *a long iron bar with shackles and a lock used to restrict the feet of prisoners; bilboes*

   farrago – *a confused mixture; farragoes*

   chiaroscuro – *pictorial art using light and shade; chiaroscuros*

   (b)

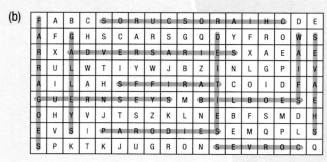

Plurals – 2

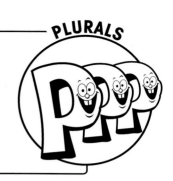

A **plural** is a word used to indicate more than one.

When a word ends in a **vowel** followed by **y**—just add **s**.
When a word ends in a **consonant** followed by **y**—change **y** to **i** and add **es**.

The plural form of words ending in **f**, can be either **fs** or **ves**.
The plural form of words ending in **o**, can be either **os** or **oes**.
If you are unsure, check the dictionary and use the first plural form listed.

1. (a) Use a dictionary to find these words. Write the plural and a definition of each word.

Singular	Definition	Plural
galley		
adversary		
guernsey		
parody		
deity		
tariff		
waif		
corf		
sheaf		
bilbo		
farrago		
chiaroscuro		

(b) Find the plural form of each word in the word search puzzle.

F	A	B	C	S	O	R	U	C	S	O	R	A	I	H	C	D	E
A	F	G	H	S	C	A	R	S	G	Q	D	Y	F	R	O	W	S
R	X	A	D	V	E	R	S	A	R	I	E	S	X	A	E	A	E
R	U	L	W	T	I	Y	W	J	B	Z	I	N	L	G	P	I	V
A	I	L	A	H	S	F	F	I	R	A	T	C	O	I	D	F	A
G	U	E	R	N	S	E	Y	S	M	B	I	L	B	O	E	S	E
O	H	Y	V	J	T	S	Z	K	L	N	E	B	F	S	M	D	H
E	V	S	I	P	A	R	O	D	I	E	S	E	M	Q	P	L	S
S	P	K	T	K	J	U	G	R	O	N	S	E	V	R	O	C	Q

Understanding and choosing words
Prefixes

PREFIXES

Focus

Prefixes: **micro**, **anti**, **fore** and **semi**

Definition

- A **prefix** is a letter or group of letters added to the beginning of a word to alter its meaning and form a new word.

Explanation

- A prefix is a word part that has a meaning of its own, often derived from Greek or Latin. Prefixes do not usually occur as independent words. The prefix is added to the beginning of a base word to change its meaning, without changing the spelling of that word. Sometimes a hyphen is placed between the prefix and the base (or root) word, such as in the following:

– When prefixes come before proper nouns.

  Example:

    un-Australian, anti-American

– When prefixes ending in **a** or **i** are added to a word that begins with the same letter.

  Example:

    ultra-ambitious

– When the prefix is **ex** or **self**, except for **selfish** and **selfless**.

  Example:

    ex-husband, self-centred

- Ensure pupils learn to be aware of letter clusters that look like prefixes, but aren't.

  Example:

    the letters **un** in **un**cle, or **in** in **in**vented

  Pupils can practise identifying these 'trick' prefixes by looking at the base or root word that is left. The prefixes that cause the most difficulty are **re**, **in** and **dis**.

- Learning the meanings of prefixes can help pupils decipher, spell and understand words, especially larger words, and increase their vocabulary. Understanding that the spelling of neither the prefix nor the base word changes can help pupils to spell commonly misspelled words such as *unnecessary*, *misspell* and *disappointment*.

- **Micro** is a prefix of Greek origin that usually refers to an object as being very small.

  Example:

    microwave, **micro**scope, **micro**phone,

    micro-organism, **micro**chip

- **Semi** can mean **half** (as in **semi**circle) or **partly** as in **semi**precious.

- **Fore** can mean **front**.

  Example:

    forehead, **fore**leg or be**fore**/in advance
    foretell, **fore**word

- **Anti** is a prefix from Greek that means **against**, **not** or **opposite**.

  Example:

    antisocial, **anti**septic

Worksheet information

- Discuss prefixes and their frequent use in English. Explain that they have their own meanings, need to be attached to words and how they change the meaning of that word.

- Divide pupils into small groups and give each group a worksheet and allow them a few minutes to choose two of the listed prefixes.

- Explain they have 10 minutes to make a list of words with the prefixes they have chosen and to write them on their sheet. They may not use any resources other than their own knowledge. Explain they should not worry about spelling the words correctly or knowing what the words mean; they should just generate a good list of words.

- At the completion of the time period, give the pupils time to guess the meaning of their prefixes and to write them on their worksheet. Pupils then use dictionaries to read definitions for their words.

- Ask the pupils to find a group that chose at least one different prefix. Pupils discuss the meanings of the prefixes they chose and correct each other as appropriate.

- To conclude, ask each group for the definitions of their prefixes and write them on the board. As a class, decide upon suitable and correct definitions for each prefix. Pupils should write them on their worksheets.

Ideas for further practice

- Label some sticky notes with prefixes and base words, ensuring each sticky note will have at least one word-forming match. Give each pupil a sticky note to attach to his/her shirt. Then pupils mingle around the room and try to find another pupil with whom they can form a word. When they find their 'match', pupil pairs can say the new word together and use that word in a sentence.

Answers

Teacher check

Prefix detectives

A **prefix** is added to the front of a word to change its meaning and make a new word. There are many prefixes that mean 'not' or 'opposite to'.

1. (a) Choose two of the following prefixes:

   micro, anti, fore and **semi**

   (b) Without looking in a dictionary, write words you know with these two prefixes.

   (c) Use a dictionary to check your guesses and correct your spelling. Discuss your definitions with another group.

	Prefix 1	Prefix 2
Words		
Predicted meaning of the prefix		
Class definition of the prefix		

2. How did other groups' definitions compare to yours?

Understanding and choosing words

Suffixes

Focus

Suffixes: **tion**, **cion**, **sion**, **ible** and **able**.

Definition

- A **suffix** is a letter or group of letters added to the end of a base word to change its meaning and form a new word.

Explanation

- The suffixes **tion**, **cion** and **sion** are often added to verbs to change them into nouns.

- There is no simple spelling rule regarding **ible** and **able**. There are, however, many more words ending in **able** than ible. Often words that have negative forms created by adding the prefixes **il**, **im**, **in**, or **ir** have **ible** suffixes.

  Example:

    illegible, inedible, irresponsible

- Verbs ending in a silent **e** usually drop that **e** when these suffixes are added, unless it is needed to keep a **c** or **g** soft.

  Example:

    sense—sensible

    knowledge—knowledgeable

- Knowing the meanings of common suffixes can help in working out the meaning of unfamiliar words. A good knowledge of suffixes will also help pupils spell correctly, develop their vocabulary, and identify what part of speech (noun, verb, adjective, adverb) the word belongs to.

Worksheet information

- Read the definition of suffixes with the pupils. Explain how a suffix is a part of a word that often has its own meaning and so changes the meaning of the word it joins.

- Pupils complete the worksheet by adding **ion** to the base words in Question 1. They should be encouraged to use a dictionary when completing Question 2 and 3.

Ideas for further practice

- Pupils could find words with the focus suffixes in newspaper articles. They write the word down with a definition for it, and break the word into base word and suffix; for example:

Word	Base word	Suffix	Meaning

- Give pupils an empty nine-square bingo grid sheet. Allow them to write one suffix in each of the nine squares on their sheet. Teacher (or a pupil) calls words from a list of base words that can have the focus suffixes added. Pupils see if any of their words can add that suffix to form a new word. If so they write the new word in that square. The first pupil to have a complete grid is the winner.

Answers

1.

1.	a	n	i	m	a	t	
2.	c	o	l	l	i	s	
3.	a	f	f	e	c	t	
4.	d	e	t	e	n	t	ion
5.	e	d	u	c	a	t	
6.	m	i	g	r	a	t	
7.	i	n	f	e	c	t	
8.	c	o	r	r	o	s	
9.	s	u	s	p	i	c	

The word is academics.

2. (a) horrible   (b) sensible
   (c) dependable   (d) comfortable
   (e) terrible   (f) breakable

3. Teacher check

Suffixes that sound similar

Suffixes are letters joined to the end of words to make new words.

The suffixes **cion**, **sion** and **tion** sound similar and often change the spelling of the base word making a verb into a noun.

For example: educate—educa**tion**, suspect—suspi**cion**, suspend—suspen**sion**

1. Use the verb clues to write the nouns ending in **ion**. The first letters of each of the words will form a word, reading from top to bottom.

Verb clues

1. animate
2. collide
3. affect
4. detain
5. educate
6. migrate
7. infect
8. corrode
9. suspect

The word is:

_____

	1.						**ion**
	2.						
	3.						
	4.						
	5.						
	6.						
	7.						
	8.						
	9.						

The suffixes **ible** and **able** often sound the same. They change words to adjectives.

For example: wash – wash**able** (able to be washed)

replace – replace**able** (can be replaced)

2. Add **ible** or **able** to these words to make adjectives.

(a) horror _____

(b) sense _____

(c) depend _____

(d) comfort _____

(e) terror _____

(f) break _____

3. Think of another word ending in **ible** and one ending in **able** and write a sentence for each.

• _____

_____

• _____

_____

Understanding and choosing words

Synonyms and antonyms

Focus

Synonyms and antonyms

Definition

- **Synonyms** are words that have the same or similar meaning.

  Example:

  unfriendly – hostile

- **Antonyms** are words that are opposite in meaning.

  Example:

  sensible — foolish

Explanation

- Identifying antonyms and synonyms develops and enriches pupils' vocabulary and enhances their written and verbal communication.

- Identifying and using more 'interesting' synonyms, such as other words for 'get' or 'went', can give more meaning to a sentence or more interest to a description.

- Antonyms and synonyms are often used as clues for crossword puzzles.

- As words can have many meanings, the context in which the word is used must be taken into consideration.

Worksheet information

- Allow pupils to read the definitions of synonyms and antonyms then give examples of each. Give further practice by asking pupils to give synonyms and antonyms of specific words. Repeat the exercise by asking pupils to give both an antonym and a synonym of specific words.

- Pupils should then be able to complete the table independently.

- The text in Question 2(a), which the pupils can read independently, includes many antonyms which have been created by adding a prefix to a base word. After they have been highlighted, circled or underlined, pupils can easily complete Question 2(b).

- Question 3 provides extra activities to reinforce synonyms and antonyms. Pupils will need a dictionary to complete Question 3(c).

Ideas for further practice

- Create crossword puzzles or wordsearches using antonyms or synonyms.

- Use 'dis' and 'il' to create antonyms. Try to work out a rule for using specific prefixes when creating antonyms;

  (The prefix 'im' is used when the base word begins with 'b', 'm', or 'p'; 'il' before 'l' and 'ir' before 'r'.)

- Write descriptions then rewrite them using synonyms. Repeat using antonyms.

Answers

1. Some possible answers are given in the table.

SYNONYM	WORD	ANTONYM
mystery, riddle	puzzle	solution
brag	boast	humble (oneself)
first, original	primary	secondary
refuse	deny	admit
empty	vacant	full
self-acting	automatic	manual
tidy	neat	messy, untidy
unite, join	combine	separate

2. (a) impossible, inaccurate, indifferent, impolite, immodest, indestructible, immature, independent, insatiable, infrequent, indecent, inadequate

   (b)
(i)	possible	(ii)	accurate
(iii)	different	(iv)	polite
(v)	modest	(vi)	destructible
(vii)	mature	(viii)	dependent
(ix)	satiable	(x)	frequent
(xi)	decent	(xii)	adequate

3. (a) Teacher check

   (b) irregular, incomplete, immortal, impatient, impractical, impersonal, imperfect, impermanent, insensitive, inactive, incorrect, inexperience, ineffective, inhumane, infinite

   (c) Teacher check

Synonyms and antonyms

Synonyms are words with the same or similar meaning.
Antonyms are words with the opposite meaning.

1. Complete the table to give a synonym and antonym for each word.

SYNONYM	WORD	ANTONYM
	puzzle (noun)	
	boast	
	primary	
	deny	
	vacant	
	automatic	
	neat	
	combine	

2. (a) Read the text below and highlight the words beginning with **-im** or **-in**.

The film premiere of 'Metal Man 2' was held this weekend at cinemas around the country. It was thought impossible for the sequel to come close to the success of the first film. However, those predictions proved totally inaccurate as even indifferent film-goers were won over by the impolite and immodest humour of the indestructible but immature hero. This independent production satisfied the insatiable desire of even infrequent viewers and blasted box office figures to an almost indecent level.

Film-goers will wonder if the next release from this production company will prove inadequate by comparison.

(b) Many antonyms are created by the prefix **-im** or **-in** which means 'not'. Write the opposites of these words used in the text.

(i) impossible _____

(ii) inaccurate _____

(iii) indifferent _____

(iv) impolite _____

(v) immodest _____

(vi) indestructible _____

(vii) immature _____

(viii) independent _____

(ix) insatiable _____

(x) infrequent _____

(xi) indecent _____

(xii) inadequate _____

3. On the back of the worksheet:

(a) write synonyms for as many words above as you can, and

(b) use prefixes such as '-im', '-in' or '-ir' to write antonyms of the following words:

regular	complete	mortal	patient	practical	personal	perfect	permanent
sensitive	active	correct	experience	effective	humane	finite	

(c) Use a dictionary to find the meanings of the words you wrote.

Understanding and choosing words

Word origins

Focus

Word origins

Definition

- **Etymology** is the name given to the systematic study of historical linguistic change, usually when referring to individual words; the body of knowledge relating to this study; an account of the history of a particular word and the derivation of a word.

  Example:

  > **century** *comes from the Latin word 'centuria' or 'centum' meaning one hundred*

Explanation

- Understanding word origins expands pupils' vocabulary and their ability to determine the meaning of unfamiliar words.
- The word part can be used as a suffix.

  Example:

  > **spire** *meaning 'breathe' (tran***spire***),*

  or as a prefix,

  Example:

  > **octo**- *meaning 'eight' (***octo***genarian)*

- In a good dictionary, word origins are usually given after the meaning of a word.

Worksheet information

- Using common root words to build words can be used to introduce the lesson and provide opportunities to practise finding and listing words from the bases provided. Pupils will need access to a good dictionary.
- Pupils should read the introduction and the text. The number of words highlighted reflects the diversity of words from other languages.
- The spelling of the sources of the words in the text gives a good indication of the words to be identified in the text.
- In Question 2, pupils use the origin meaning to give a definition.

  Example:

  > *restaurant: a place where people can go to eat food and feel restored*

Ideas for further practice

- Use a dictionary or reputable Internet sources to find the origins of the other words in the text which were not included in Questions 1 and 2—*celebrating, octogenarian, pizza, spaghetti, related, travelling, telephone.*
- List common root words on charts for an easy reference for writing.

Answers

1. (a) anecdotes   (b) arthritis
   (c) coach   (d) concession
   (e) craft   (f) dinner
   (g) enjoyed   (h) Friday
   (i) suffers   (j) family
   (k) journey   (l) learning
   (m) voyage

2. Teacher check. Answers will be similar to:

   (a) *restaurant* – an establishment where meals are served to customers.

   (b) *antipasto* – an assortment of meats, cheeses, olives, etc., served as an appetiser

   (c) *incredible* – cannot be believed

   (d) *dynamo* – a forceful, energetic person

   (e) *cruise* – to sail to and fro, or from place to place for pleasure

   (f) *second* – after first in order, a measure of time

Word origins

Etymology is the study of word origins.
Many of the words we use come from other languages.
Knowing where words come from and their meaning can help us work out
the meaning of some unknown words.

1. Select from the highlighted words to match the clues below.

> On **Friday,** our **family** went to Adolpho's Italian **restaurant** for **dinner**. We were **celebrating** with Grandma, who has become an **octogenarian**. We **enjoyed** our meal of **antipasto**, **pizza**, **spaghetti** and gelato while Grandma **related incredible anecdotes** about her life as a youngster. Although she **suffers** from **arthritis** and has an old-age **concession** card, she is still a **dynamo**. She always seems to be taking a **journey** by **coach** or a **voyage** on a **cruise** ship. When she is not **travelling** around, she is **learning** a new **craft**. Usually Mum or Dad **telephone** her every **second** day or so to see if she is okay but she seems to think that she is being babied or treated like an old lady. I hope Gran never changes!

(a) **anekdota** – things unpublished _____

(b) **nosos arthritis** – disease of the joints _____

(c) **kotsche** – large kind of carriage _____

(d) **concessionem** – right granted by government _____

(e) **croeft** – skill, art, strength _____

(f) **disner** – (originally) take the first meal of the day _____

(g) **enjoir** – to give joy, rejoice _____

(h) **frigedaeg** – Frigga's day _____

(i) **suffrir** – undergo, endure _____

(j) **familia** – household (relatives and servants) _____

(k) **journée** – day's work or travel _____

(l) **leornian** – to get knowledge, be cultivated _____

(m) **veiage** – travel, journey _____

2. Write a definition for each word below using the information about word origins provided in brackets and the context in which these words were used in the text.

(a) restaurant (food that restores) _____

(b) antipasto (before food) _____

(c) incredible (trust, believe) _____

(d) dynamo (power) _____

(e) cruise (to cross, sail to and fro) _____

(f) second (following, next in order) _____

Understanding and choosing words

Confused words

Focus

Words that look and sound similar

Explanation

- Some of the pairs of words have completely different meanings. Confusion occurs because the words have similar sounds and/or spellings.

Worksheet information

- The answers to the clues are examples of commonly confused pairs of words, some of which are related. Before completing the puzzle, write the pairs of words on the board and discuss their sounds, spelling, definitions and parts of speech within the context of a given sentence.

  emigrant – immigrant

  export – import

  accept – except

  uninterested – disinterested

  access – excess

  device – devise

  advice – advise

  affect – affect

  breath – breathe

- Pupils complete the puzzle.

Ideas for further practice

- Write each word on a piece of card. Pupils lay the cards face down and take turns to choose a card and compose a sentence containing the word. The other pupils name the part of speech the word takes within the sentence.

- Create a class book of frequently confused words. Use them to write sentences for dictation.

- On card, pupils write cloze sentences for each pair of words, writing in brackets the pair of words from which a choice is to be made to complete the sentence. On separate card, pupils write the answers for their sentences. Collect the cards and use them as a class resource.

- Assign pairs of words to one of two piles: those that are related in meaning and those that have completely different meanings.

Answers

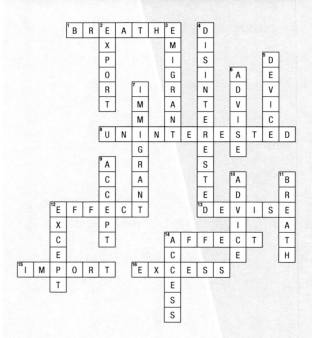

Confused Words – 1

Some related words sound and look similar but have different meanings.

Find pairs of commonly confused words to complete the puzzle.

Down

2. To send (goods and services) to another country
3. A person who leaves his or her country to live in another
4. Not directly involved in something
5. An invention that does something
6. To offer suggestions to someone
7. A person who comes into a new country, intending to make it home
9. To receive something willingly
10. An opinion given to help with a decision
11. The air inhaled through the mouth and nose and expelled from the lungs
12. To exclude or leave out
14. The right of coming to or approaching

Across

1. To take in and expel air
8. Not wanting to know about something
12. The result of some action
13. To think out or invent a plan
14. To cause a change in something
15. To bring (goods and services) in from another country
16. An overabundance

Understanding and choosing words

Confused words

Focus

Words related to quantity

Explanation

- **between/among**

  Between is used when referring to two of anything.

  Example:

  > share **between** two people

  > walk **between** two cars

  Among is used when referring to three or more.

  Example:

  > walk **among** the flowers

  > share **among** the class

- **fewer/less**

  Fewer is used when the number can be counted individually.

  Example:

  > There are **fewer** eggs in this basket.

  Less is used when referring to quantities and qualities that cannot be counted.

  Example:

  > **less** sunshine, **less** active, **less** time

- **couple/few/several**

  Couple is generally accepted to mean two.

  Example:

  > a married **couple**, a **couple** of days

  Few refers to a small number or amount.

  Example:

  > a **few** cars, a **few** spots of rain

  Several refers to a greater number or amount than a few, but it is not excessive.

  Example:

  > **Several** children at the playground.

Worksheet information

- Clearly explain the rules for using **between/among** and **fewer/less**.
- **Couple/few/several** are more reliant on the context in which they are used rather than a hard and fast rule. There may be clues in the text to indicate the correct choice of words as in Question 3 of the cloze procedure. The word **of** follows the gap and so **few** cannot be used.

Ideas for further practice

- Write the seven quantity words on separate cards. In groups, the pupils choose a card and give a sentence containing the word. The rest of the group determine if the word has been used correctly.
- Pupils write notes on how and when each word is used then explain to a group of pupils in the year below.
- In groups, pupils write cloze sentences requiring the seven words to be inserted. The sentences are shared around the group, completed individually and then discussed as a group.

Answers

1.   (a) between   (b) among   (c) fewer
       (d) Fewer   (e) A couple of (f) a few
       (g) several

2.   Teacher check

3.   1. Several   2. few/couple   3. couple
       4. couple/few 5. among   6. fewer
       7. between   8. less   9. among

Confused Words – 2

Some words related to quantity can be confused.

1. **Circle the correct word.**

   (a) The twins shared the treats **between / among** them.

   (b) The dog ran **between / among** the flock of birds.

   (c) There were **fewer / less** pupils absent from school today.

   (d) **Fewer / Less** people attend the local team's home matches these days.

   (e) A **couple of / A few / Several** birds are nesting in the box.

   (f) It's been **a couple of / a few / several** days since I fell over but my leg still hurts.

   (g) Even after **a couple of / a few / several** years, nothing would grow in the contaminated soil.

2. **Write a sentence for each word.**

   between: _____

   among: _____

   fewer: _____

   less: _____

   couple: _____

   few: _____

   several: _____

3. **Read the text and insert the appropriate word from the box.**

between	among	fewer	less	couple	few	several

   ## ❦ The dinner party ❦

   The guests arrived as the sun was going down. _____[1] people arrived in

   their cars while a _____[2] braved the overgrown path that lead from the village to our

   house, which was just a _____[3] of kilometres away. Mum and Dad had allowed me to

   invite a _____[4] of my friends to help out.

   We circulated _____[5] the guests, offering them canapes and drinks as they arrived.

   There were two minor mishaps, _____[6] than Mum had expected! As the guests went

   in to dinner, Mum and Dad shared the servant role _____[7] them.

   My friends and I headed to the kitchen to clear up. There was _____[8] mess than we

   thought there would be. We were soon able to divide the leftover food _____[9] us

   before waiting for our next job.

Punctuation

Punctuation marks and capital letters

Focus

Capital letters for sentence beginnings and proper nouns

Full stops at the end of a sentence and for abbreviations

Question marks

Exclamation marks

Definitions

- **Full stops** are punctuation marks used to show the end of a sentence.

- An **abbreviation** is a shortened form of a word.

  A full stop can be used to show that a word has been abbreviated.

  Example:

  telephone — tel. or continued — cont.

- **Question marks** are punctuation marks used to indicate a question.

- **Exclamation marks** are punctuation marks used at the end of a remark to show strong emotion or feeling.

  Example:

  Oh no! I left it on the kitchen table!

Explanation

- Full stops usually show the end of an idea or thought in a sentence. They can also indicate that a break is needed when reading.

- In abbreviations, full stops are not used when the last letter is the last letter of the word.*

  Example:

  Rd, St, Dr

- The necessity for faster communication has contributed to some changes.

- Abbreviations of proper nouns, such as New South Wales (NSW) no longer need full stops. They are now only used to avoid confusion.

- A question is an interrogative statement, addressed to someone in order to elicit information.

- Exclamation marks usually indicate strong feeling, such as surprise, disgust or anger. An exclamation mark can be used at the end of an interjection (*Oh no!*) or command (*Don't touch!*) and to add emphasis.

Worksheet information

- Revise the information about full stops, question marks, exclamation marks, abbreviations and capital letters, giving some examples before allowing the pupils to complete the worksheet.

- NOTE: The text on page 59 has been written to utilise specific words and is in no way intended to tell pupils the correct way to write assignments.

Ideas for further practice

- Revise incorrectly-identified errors in future grammar lessons.

- Provide pupils with opportunities to edit punctuation in other texts, including the work of other pupils.

Answers

1. **Mr B**annerman, our class teacher, is helping us get ready for **G**illespie **S**econdary **S**chool. **F**rom **May**, until the time that we leave in **July**, he is helping us to complete assignments in the same way that our secondary teachers will expect. **I**t sounded really hard to me at first**! H**ow much work would we have to do**?**

   First, we needed to be able to write a well-constructed paragraph with an introductory sentence and supporting information. **T**hat wasn't too hard**! I**t was just like writing a different type of story. **W**ho couldn't follow a set of guidelines to do that**? I** could**!**

   Next, we needed to be able to refer to a chapter in a particular book. **W**e also needed to be able to include diagrams and a figure if the text needs them. **B**oth of those were easy**! F**inally, we needed to be able to add an appendix if necessary. **T**here are so many things to do**! W**ill we be able to remember them all**? I** hope so**!**

2. Refer to wordsearch solution

R	F	C	O	N	T	I	N	U	E	D	V	Y	B
I	B	B	C	X	D	N	A	L	S	I	K	F	
V	G	A	A	S	S	O	C	I	A	T	I	O	N
E	P	I	N	C	O	R	P	O	R	A	T	E	D
R	P	R	O	F	E	S	S	O	R	W	M	S	E
Y	N	A	P	M	O	C	R	Y	A	D	I	R	F
J	H	T	A	I	L	A	R	T	S	U	A	T	X
Y	L	B	A	B	O	R	P	A	U	S	U	A	L
G	O	V	E	R	N	O	R	G	L	E	G	A	P
A	P	R	I	L	J	S	S	C	H	O	O	L	S
H	T	T	E	L	E	P	H	O	N	E	J	W	J

> * Prim-Ed Publishing employs full stops for abbreviations as recommended by the ***Style manual for authors, editors and printers, sixth edition, 2002***.

Punctuation marks and capital letters

1. Edit the text below to include full stops, capital letters for sentence beginnings, capital letters for proper nouns, exclamation marks and question marks.

   Write your corrections above each error.

   mr bannerman, our class teacher, is helping us get ready for gillespie secondary school from may, until the time that we leave in july, he is helping us to complete assignments in the same way that our secondary teachers will expect it sounded really hard to me at first how much work would we have to do

   first, we needed to be able to write a well-constructed paragraph with an introductory sentence and supporting information that wasn't too hard it was just like writing a different type of story who couldn't follow a set of guidelines to do that i could

   next, we needed to be able to refer to a chapter in a particular book we also needed to be able to include diagrams and a figure if the text needs them both of those were easy finally, we needed to be able to add an appendix if necessary there are so many things to do will we be able to remember them all i hope so

   FULL STOPS

   EXCLAMATION MARKS

   QUESTION MARKS

   CAPITAL LETTERS

2. Find complete words in the word search using the abbreviation clues.

   > Words such as 'September', 'paragraph', 'chapter', and 'appendix' can be abbreviated to 'Sept.', 'para.', 'chap.' and 'app.' using full stops.

   (a) tel.
   (b) cont.
   (c) Co.
   (d) Is.
   (e) Inc.
   (f) p.
   (g) Apr.
   (h) sch.
   (i) Aust.
   (j) assoc.
   (k) Gov.
   (l) prob.
   (m) riv.
   (n) Prof.
   (o) usu.
   (p) Fri.

R	F	C	O	N	T	I	N	U	E	D	V	Y	B
I	B	B	C	X	D	N	A	L	S	I	I	K	F
V	G	A	A	S	S	O	C	I	A	T	I	O	N
E	P	I	N	C	O	R	P	O	R	A	T	E	D
R	P	R	O	F	E	S	S	O	R	W	M	S	E
Y	N	A	P	M	O	C	R	Y	A	D	I	R	F
J	H	T	A	I	L	A	R	T	S	U	A	T	X
K	Y	L	B	A	B	O	R	P	U	S	U	A	L
G	O	V	E	R	N	O	R	G	L	E	G	A	P
A	P	R	I	L	J	S	S	C	H	O	O	L	S
H	T	T	E	L	E	P	H	O	N	E	J	W	J

Punctuation

Commas

Focus

Commas in a series of words, clauses and phrases

Commas in the middle of a sentence to set off a phrase or clause

Definitions

- **Commas** are punctuation marks used to separate words, phrases or clauses to clarify meaning.
- A **phrase** is a group of words in a sentence which does not have a finite verb (i.e. a verb with a subject).
- A **clause** is a group of words, including a verb and its subject. (A clause can be a simple sentence.)

Explanation

- In a series, the comma stands for an omitted conjunction, such as 'and' or 'or'.

  Example:

  'I play the violin, cello and piano' means 'I play the violin and cello and piano'. The comma has replaced the omitted 'and'.

- Commas can be used for:

  – a series of nouns.

  Example:

  The meal consisted of steak, peas and potatoes.

  – a series of verbs.

  Example:

  Jason ran, tripped, fell and fainted.

  – a series of adjectives.

  Example:

  She was young, beautiful, kind and naive.

  – a series of phrases.

  Example:

  He doesn't like washing dishes, ironing clothes or mopping floors.

- A pair of commas can be used in the middle of a sentence to set off a phrase or clause which is not essential to the meaning of the sentence. The first comma indicates the beginning of the phrase or clause and the second indicates the end of that phrase or clause.

  Example:

  That girl, wearing blue pyjamas, is my sister.

Worksheet information

- Read the text with the class. Pupils identify the sentences with lists of words, and the sentence with the lists of phrases or clauses. Explain that a phrase is a group of words which can form a unit in a sentence. It does not contain a subject 'doing' a verb. A clause does have a verb with a subject.
- Read about using commas with clauses or phrases which provide additional information within the text. Provide some basic examples of phrases or clauses for the pupils or ask pupils to share their own ideas.
- Pupils complete Questions 2, 3 and 4.

Ideas for further practice

- Finish the sentence. 'Four animals which live in the Arctic are …'; 'To make a pizza, we need …' Create your own sentence starters.
- Find a suitable newspaper article, copy it and distribute to the class. Pupils identify sentences which contain lists of words, clauses and phrases and highlight them.
- Pupils work in pairs. One pupil writes the sentence (missing the phrase or clause) while at the same time the other pupil (without looking at the first pupil's sentence) writes a phrase or clause. The two are put together to create a silly sentence.

Answers

1. Teacher check

2. (a) a tropical fruit

   (b) providing Mum agrees

3. (a) That man, loitering near the ATM, looks very suspicious. I think I'll avoid using the machine for my banking today.

   (b) My favourite film, which also happens to be a classic book, is 'The lion, the witch and the wardrobe'.

4. Teacher check

Commas

> **Commas** are used to separate a series of words, phrases or clauses in a sentence to make the meaning clear.

1. (a) Read the text.

> *It was time to start planning our next family holiday. We sat down for our family meeting to decide where we would go, how we would get there, what we would like to do once we were there and how we would get the money together. I always loved these meetings. I really enjoyed the negotiating, planning, organising and debating. Mum, Dad, Marty, Susan and I always took some time to agree on a holiday destination. In order to keep everyone happy, we usually made a list of what each of us would like to do, we searched the Internet to find a location which would accommodate most activities and we finally agreed on the venue. We then each took a task to help in the organisation and planning of our holiday. I had to research the accommodation, Dad had to research our travel arrangements, Mum had to find out about transport, Marty had to calculate how much the activities were going to cost and Susan was responsible for making a suggested itinerary. We had to complete our tasks and report back one week later.*

   (b) Circle all the commas used in lists of words, phrases and clauses.

   (c) Use a coloured pencil to underline words, phrases and clauses used in lists.

> **Commas** are used to identify a phrase or clause in a sentence which provides the reader with extra background information. If this extra information is taken out, the sentence will still make sense.

2. Underline the phrase or clause which gives extra information in each of these sentences.

   (a) Pawpaw, a tropical fruit, is considered very valuable because of its healing properties.

   (b) I'm hoping, providing Mum agrees, to invite four friends over for a slumber party for my birthday.

3. Use commas to identify the phrase or clause providing extra information in each of these sentences.

   (a) That man loitering near the ATM looks very suspicious. I think I'll avoid using the machine for my banking today.

   (b) My favourite film which also happens to be a classic book is 'The lion, the witch and the wardrobe'.

4. Write a phrase or clause to complete each sentence and add any necessary commas.

   (a) The firefighters _____ as they worked feverishly to battle the enormous flames coming from the factory.

   (b) The green sea turtle _____ is so named because of the layer of body fat which is green from the algae it eats.

Punctuation

Commas

COMMAS

Focus

Commas used to join two or more simple sentences

Definition

- **Commas** are punctuation marks used to separate words or phrases to clarify meaning.

Explanation

- Commas can be used with a conjunction to join two simple sentences into a longer, more complex sentence.
- The most common sentence type is the simple sentence. Too many simple sentences in writing can make the writing seem childish. Joining two or more simple sentences to make a complex or compound sentence can add a sense of maturity and interest to the text.

Worksheet information

- Read the information and examples provided. Ask pupils to offer simple sentences of their own. Use these to demonstrate and practise joining two or more simple sentences together.
- Pupils identify the simple sentences within each sentence.
- Pupils then practise joining simple sentences.

Ideas for further practice

- Find a suitable newspaper article, copy it and distribute to the class. Pupils identify simple sentences and practise joining them. Identify more complex sentences with a comma used to combine two or more simple sentences.
- Pupils work in pairs. One pupil writes one simple sentence while at the same time the other pupil (without looking at the first pupil's sentence) writes another simple sentence. The two are put together to create a silly sentence.

Answers

1. (a) <u>I mowed the lawn</u>, so <u>Jayden trimmed the edges</u>.

   (b) <u>The sun melted the snow</u>, then <u>in one hour it had totally disappeared</u>.

   (c) <u>Mum went shopping on Saturday</u>, while <u>Dad took us to the cinema</u>.

   (d) <u>Bradley went swimming at the beach</u>, but <u>I built enormous sandcastles</u>.

   (e) <u>Dad wouldn't let me go to the party</u>, so <u>I threw a huge tantrum</u>.

2. Teacher check. Possible answers include:

   (a) Barry likes to eat fried rice, **so** he eats it at least once a week.

   (b) Our cat is getting very old, **so** we pay special attention to her.

   (c) It is important to eat a balanced diet, **so** Mum makes sure we eat the right amount from each food group each day.

   (d) **Although** natural honey is great on toast for breakfast, it is also known for its fantastic healing properties on wounds and ulcers.

   (e) We all know that it is important to exercise for at least 30 minutes each day, **yet** so many of us are lucky if we do 30 minutes of exercise in one week.

Commas joining simple sentences

A *comma*, together with a *conjunction*, can be used to join together two or more simple sentences to make your writing more interesting.

For example: My friend invited me to a party. I do not want to go.

My friend invited me to a party *but* I do not want to go.

Although my friend invited me to a party, I do not want to go.

1. Underline each simple sentence.

(a) I mowed the lawn, so Jayden trimmed the edges.

(b) The sun melted the snow, then in one hour it had totally disappeared.

(c) Mum went shopping on Saturday, while Dad took us to the cinema.

(d) Bradley went swimming at the beach, but I built enormous sandcastles.

(e) Dad wouldn't let me go to the party, so I threw a huge tantrum.

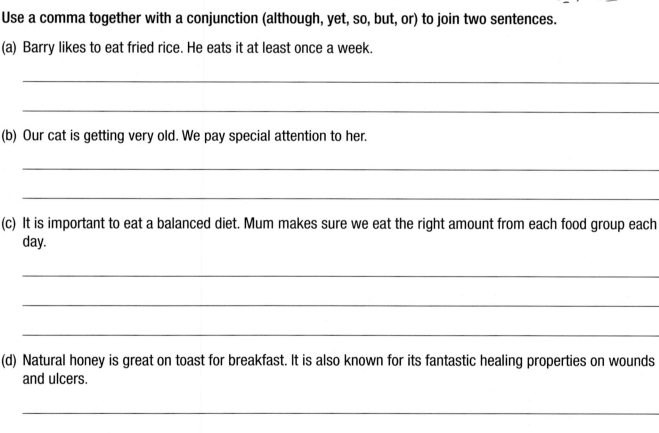

2. Use a comma together with a conjunction (although, yet, so, but, or) to join two sentences.

(a) Barry likes to eat fried rice. He eats it at least once a week.

_____

_____

(b) Our cat is getting very old. We pay special attention to her.

_____

_____

(c) It is important to eat a balanced diet. Mum makes sure we eat the right amount from each food group each day.

_____

_____

_____

(d) Natural honey is great on toast for breakfast. It is also known for its fantastic healing properties on wounds and ulcers.

_____

_____

_____

(e) We all know that it is important to exercise for at least 30 minutes each day. So many of us are lucky if we do 30 minutes of exercise in one week.

_____

_____

_____

Punctuation

Apostrophes

Focus

Apostrophes in contractions

Definition

- A **contraction** is a shorter word made by joining two or more words and taking out one or more letters. The missing letter or letters is/are replaced by an apostrophe.

Explanation

- When two or more words are joined and contracted, the omitted letters are marked with an apostrophe.

- The mistake is often made of placing the apostrophe between the two words, e.g. **should'nt**, **do'nt**. Pupils will need to be reminded that the apostrophe marks the missing letter and not the space where the two words join.

- Contractions are commonly used in speech and informal writing, but not often in formal writing.

- Not all words with apostrophes are contractions. Apostrophes can also indicate possession.

- Double contractions are common in speech; e.g. 'shouldn't've' and 'who'd've'. It is important for pupils to be aware of the correct spelling of such words; e.g 'I'd've' is sometimes pronounced 'I'da'.

Worksheet information

- Read and discuss the information in the introduction on the pupil page. After reading the pirate story, ask pupils to suggest the meanings of the unusual contractions, but do not provide them with the definitions as they will need to work them out in Question 1(b).

- Pupils complete Question 1(b) by drawing a line from each contraction to its definition and the words that form the contraction. Advise pupils to read the text again to help them define each contraction.

- For Question 2, pupils read the sentences and determine which word makes the 's' in the contracted word. To find the correct answer, pupils may need to try saying each word (**is, has** and **us**) after the first half of the contraction.

- In Question 3, pupils say the contracted word then write the words it is made from.

Ideas for further practice

- There are a number of online interactive games where pupils can practise contracting words. Try <*http://www.primarygames.com/contractions/start. htm*>, <*http://www.quia.com/jg/86241.html*>

Answers

1. (a) man-o'-war, fo'c'sle, Cap'n, ne'er-do-well, Cap'n, will-o'-the-wisp, cat-o'-nine-tails
   (b) front part of ship – fo'c'sle – forecastle
   a whip with nine 'tails' – cat-o'-nine tails – cat of nine tails
   ghostly, flickering lights – will-o'-the-wisp – will of the wisp
   a sailing ship with cannons – man-o'-war – man of war
   an irresponsible or lazy person – ne'er-do-well – never do well
   according to the clock – o'clock – of the clock

2. (a) us   (b) is
   (c) has   (d) has

3. (a) They will have   (b) could not have
   (c) should not have   (d) Who would have

Apostrophes in contractions

Contractions are words made by joining two or more words and taking out some letters. The letters are replaced by an apostrophe.

Contractions are often used in speech because they are quicker and easier to say. They are not often used in writing, and hardly ever in 'formal' writing.

1. (a) Some contractions used often in the past are not as common today. Read the text and underline the 'old' contractions.

> *The pirate captain guided the man-o'-war close to the coast. He stood on the fo'c'sle and peered through his telescope to the land ahead.*
>
> *Cap'n! Look! Lights!*
>
> *'Where?' snarled the captain, his patience growing thin. 'If this be one of your tricks again, you scrawny little ne'er-do-well ...'*
>
> *'Cap'n, I swear on my own mother's life I saw lights! Maybe ... do you think ... could it be ... will-o'-the-wisp?'*
>
> *'Rubbish', growled the captain. 'You stop that superstitious nonsense or I'll take to you with the cat-o'-nine-tails!'*

(b) Draw lines to match each contraction to its meaning and the words that were shortened to make it.

front part of a ship •	(ne'er-do-well)	• man of war
a whip with nine 'tails' •	(o'clock)	• cat of nine tails
ghostly, flickering lights •	(fo'c'sle)	• of the clock
a sailing ship with cannons •	(cat-o'-nine-tails)	• forecastle
an irresponsible or lazy person •	(will-o'-the-wisp)	• never do well
according to the clock •	(man-o'-war)	• will of the wisp

2. Are these contractions ending in 's' contractions of 'is', 'has', or 'us'? Colour the correct boxes.

(a) C'mon everyone! Let's go!

us	has	is

(b) She's a great athlete, isn't she?

us	has	is

(c) Liam's got an awesome new phone.

us	has	is

(d) It's been ages since I read that book.

us	has	is

3. Some words have 'double contractions'—for example, should'nt've (should not have)—which are spoken but rarely written. Read the sentences and write which words make up the contractions.

(a) They'll've eaten all the food by the time we get there! _____

(b) It couldn't've been me! I wasn't even there! _____

(c) I shouldn't've eaten that pie! _____

(d) Who'd've thought our Tim could have won a race! _____

Punctuation
Apostrophes

Focus

Common mistakes made when using apostrophes to show possession

Definition

- An **apostrophe** of possession indicates ownership and is placed directly after the owner/owners.

  Example:

  The girl's uniform was saturated (one girl).

  The girls' teacher was quite strict (more than one girl).

  The children's school was close by.

Explanation

- Many people make the mistake of adding an apostrophe to make a noun plural. Such incorrect use of apostrophes is sometimes called 'greengrocers' apostrophes' (as the mistake can often be found on handwritten signs, such as those found at the greengrocer).

Worksheet information

- Read the introductory text and common problems in the text boxes with the pupils. Discuss different ways to avoid making these mistakes. Some ideas include:

  – To work out where the apostrophe needs to go, pupils can circle the owner, add an apostrophe outside the right side of the circle, and add an 's' if there isn't one already there.

  – The possessive can often be identified by the presence of two nouns together. Pupils can check the first to see if it is possessive by substituting a possessive pronoun for it:

  Example:

  Carla's shoes (her shoes).

- Pupils then complete Questions 2 and 3, practising the correct use of the apostrophes to show ownership.

Ideas for further practice

- Pupils can practise using apostrophes correctly by doing one of the quizzes at *<http://www.bbc.co.uk/ skillswise/words/grammar/punctuation/apostrophes/ quiz.shtm>*

- Encourage pupils to look for mistakes in newspaper articles, shop signs and 'junk mail'. Bring these in and discuss how they are wrong and how the incorrect use of an apostrophe can change the meaning of the sentence.

Answers

1. Blake's, hour's, Mars', planet's, Igilpilly's, Blake's, stepbrothers', Lee's

2. (a) Blake's mum took so many **photos**, the memory card was full in five **minutes**.

   (b) Blake's family enjoyed the one week's journey to Mars' spaceport in the **2030s**.

   (c) Blake and his **stepbrothers** watched hundreds of **DVDs** on their way to **Mars**.

   (d) Blake had to carry all the **suitcases**, even Logan and Lee's **bags**.

3. (a) Maria and her brother's new kittens were making a huge mess in Nanna's house.

   (b) Kyle's photos of his family's holiday were great, especially the children's sandcastles.

   (c) The twin girls' paintings were admired by hundreds of the art show's visitors.

Apostrophes for possession

When using an **apostrophe** to show ownership, the apostrophe goes straight after the owner or owners. Most apostrophes are shaped with a tail that points to the owner.

For example: Cody's dog's ears went flat when Cody mentioned it was bathtime.
The Bruce children had many pets. The children's pets' names all started with B.

Using **apostrophes** correctly can be a bit tricky. Remember that they are used to show possession or a contraction, not plurals.

For example: Free **biscuits** with your tea. (not *free biscuit's*)

Those are my favourite **CDs**. (not **CD's**)

1. Read the text and circle the apostrophes that show possession.

> *Public space travel had begun in the 2030s, and finally it was Blake's turn. In an hour's time he would be landing on Mars' red surface. He looked out the window, keen to be the first to spot the planet's spaceport. His little stepbrother, who of course had the best seat, beat him to it.*
>
> *'Look, Mum!' cried Logan. 'There are the lights of Igilpilly's port!'*
>
> *'You mean Elegelly', snorted Lee, the older of Blake's two stepbrothers. Blake had almost had enough of his two stepbrothers' bickering. The craft landed safely and, struggling with Logan and Lee's bags, Blake stepped onto Mars, wishing he had a new family to go with his new life!*

2. Circle the mistakes then rewrite these sentences correctly.

   (a) Blakes mum took so many photo's, the memory card was full in five minute's.

   _____

   (b) Blakes family enjoyed the one weeks journey to Mar's spaceport in the 2030's.

   _____

   (c) Blake and his stepbrother's watched hundreds of DVD's on their way to Mars'.

   _____

   (d) Blake had to carry all the suitcase's, even Logan and Lees' bag's.

   _____

3. Put apostrophes in the correct place in these sentences.

   (a) Maria and her brothers new kittens were both making a huge mess in Nannas house.

   (b) Kyles photos of his familys holiday were great, especially the childrens sandcastles.

   (c) The twin girls paintings were admired by hundreds of the art shows visitors.

Punctuation
Quotation marks

Focus

Direct speech

Definitions

- **Quotation marks** are inverted commas used to enclose speech or thoughts.
- The carrier is the part of the sentence indicating who is speaking.

Explanation

- Quotation marks are used to show the exact words spoken by a person.
- A quotation always starts with a new sentence so it begins with a capital letter.
- A new paragraph is needed for each speaker.
- Indirect speech tells what was said but not in the exact words, so it does not need quotation marks.

> In direct speech, the presence and position of a carrier affects the punctuation of the quotation.
>
> The punctuation guidelines followed in this book are those outlined in the *Style manual for authors, editors and printers* (sixth edition) 2002.

When a quotation stands without a carrier—

- all words and punctuation marks are enclosed by the quotation marks:

  e.g. 'We all wish you well in your new school.'

When a carrier precedes the quotation—

- the carrier (underlined) is followed by a comma,
- the quotation begins with a capital letter,
- the final full stop of the quotation lies outside the closing quotation mark:

  e.g. <u>Tania sighed</u>, 'This is the last day of term. We have six weeks with no school'.

When a carrier interrupts a sentence within a quotation—

- the comma following the first part of the sentence lies outside its closing quotation mark,
- the speaker's name is followed by a comma,
- the sentence continues with a small letter,
- the final full stop of the quotation lies outside the closing quotation mark:

  e.g. 'I'm so glad', <u>said Isaac</u>, 'that we are on holiday'.

When a carrier interrupts a quotation between two separate sentences—

- the comma following the first sentence lies outside its closing quotation mark
- the carrier (underlined) is followed by a full stop.

- the rest of the quotation is treated as a quotation without a carrier.

  e.g. 'I'm going away for three weeks', <u>said Jayden</u>. 'We're visiting relatives in the country.'

When a carrier follows the quotation—

- the comma following the quotation lies outside its closing quotation mark,
- the carrier (underlined) is followed by a full stop:

  e.g. 'We can keep in touch via email', <u>offered Libby</u>.

Worksheet information

- Explain that the punctuation rules for this exercise may not be consistent with those they will find in many other texts containing direct speech.
- On the board, write a number of examples of direct speech and punctuate correctly using the rules on the pupil worksheet.

Ideas for further practice

- On individual cards, each pupil writes three examples of direct speech from any books he/she is currently using, omitting all punctuation, including capital letters. Use these cards as resources for pupils to practise punctuation following the guidelines of the *Style manual*.
- In pairs, pupils find examples of direct speech with the carrier always in the same position. They familiarise themselves with the punctuation rules of this example and produce a poster explaining how to punctuate it. The poster is used as an aid to explain the rules to other pupils.

Answers

1. (a) 'Please pass the salt.' (b) 'This is a delicious meal.' (c) 'I don't like the vegetables.'

2. (a) Bill said, 'Please pass the salt'. (b) Jill said, 'This is a delicious meal'. (c) Bill said, 'I don't like the vegetables'.

3. (a) 'Please pass the salt', said Bill. (b) 'This is a delicious meal', said Jill. (c) 'I don't like the vegetables', said Bill.

4. (a) Bill asked, 'Where are we going?' (b) Jill shouted, 'Watch out for that puddle!' (c) 'What puddle?' asked Bill.

5. (a) 'My socks are soaking', said Bill. 'The rain has gone right through.'

Quotation marks for direct speech

Quotation marks are inverted commas used to enclose speech or thoughts.

The **carrier** is the part of the sentence indicating who is speaking. It can be placed at the beginning, in the middle or at the end of the speech.

The opening **quotation mark** always comes just before the first word of direct speech. Knowing where to place the closing quotation mark is a little trickier!

- Each box shows a different way to write direct speech.

- The information explains where to place the closing quotation mark.

If there is no carrier: (a)

- the closing quotation mark comes after the full stop at the end of the speech:

  Example: *'Nice to see you again, Bill.'*

1. Add quotation marks.

   (a) Please pass the salt.

   (b) This is a delicious meal.

   (c) I don't like the vegetables.

If the carrier comes before the speech: (b)

- it is followed by a comma,

- the closing quotation mark comes before the final full stop:

  Example: *Jill said, 'Nice to see you again, Bill'.*

2. Add quotation marks.

   (a) Bill said, Please pass the salt.

   (b) Jill said, This is a delicious meal.

   (c) Bill said, I don't like the vegetables.

If the carrier comes after the speech: (c)

- the speech ends with a comma,

- the closing quotation mark comes before the comma:

  Example: *'Nice to see you again', said Jill.*

3. Add quotation marks.

   (a) Please pass the salt, said Bill.

   (b) This is a delicious meal, said Jill.

   (c) I don't like the vegetables, said Bill.

Wherever the carrier is: (d)

- question marks and exclamation marks always go inside the closing quotation mark:

  Example: *Jill said, 'Hurry up! We're late!'*

4. Add quotation marks.

   (a) Bill asked, Where are we going?

   (b) Jill shouted, Watch out for that puddle!

   (c) What puddle? asked Bill.

When the carrier interrupts a speech: (e)

- if it also interrupts a sentence, the sentence continues with a small letter.

  Example: 'Why is it always me', moaned Bill, 'who ends up in a mess?'

- if it separates two sentences, the second sentence is treated like a quotation without a carrier.

  Example: 'It just seems that way', comforted Jill. 'We all get in a mess sometimes.'

5. Add quotation marks.

   (a) My socks are soaking, said Bill. The rain has gone right through.

Punctuation
Quotation marks

Focus

Using quotation marks in handwritten work

Definition

- **Quotation marks** are inverted commas used to enclose speech or thoughts.

Explanation

- Quotation marks are used in writing to highlight direct speech (the actual words spoken).
  Example:
  'I had hot chocolate and muffins for afternoon tea', said Allan.

- In handwritten work, they also have many other purposes. They enclose:
  - the quoted work of other authors, including excerpts of quotations.
    Example:
    'The people of Happy Town', she wrote, 'are disappointed with the response from the town council'.
  - the title of a song, long poem, book, play, film, television or radio programme, work of art, or an article in a magazine or journal.
    Example:
    Many people read the 'No cash for hospitals' article in the morning paper.
  - colloquial references in formal writing.
    Example:
    The minister really 'put his foot in it' when he spoke disrespectfully about the visiting heads of state.
  - a term that is introduced by a word, phrase or clause such as 'labelled', 'called', 'entitled', 'the expression'.
    Example:
    The opposing team was referred to as 'The pirates'.

- Quotation marks are not used to enclose:
  - indirect speech
    Example:
    They said that the burnt bush land would regenerate.
  - well-known expressions.
    Example:
    Mr Jones was given the sack after years of loyal service.
  - words following 'so-called'.
    Example:
    The so-called champion was found to have cheated.
  - direct speech in play scripts where the reader's name precedes it.
    Example:
    Long John Silver: Well Jim-lad, you and I shall share Captain Flint's treasure.

- Single quotation marks are used for direct speech and double quotation marks are used for quotations within quotations.
  Example:
  'My favourite book is "Robinson Crusoe"', answered Sir Daniel Atterdale.

Note: When writing is typed on a word processor rather than handwritten, the use of italics replaces the need for quotation marks.

For example: The title of a book, play, long poem, film, television or radio programme, work of art, article in a magazine or journal; the name of a vehicle (land, sea or air); the Latin name of a plant or animal are all italicised.

Song titles and individually titled episodes of a television or radio programme retain single quotation marks and are not italicised.

Worksheet information

- Revise placement of quotation marks relative to other punctuation before pupils attempt the worksheet.
- If a quote is written with a carrier, the last full stop lies outside the quotation mark.
  Example:
  She said, 'For relaxation, I like to bake cakes'.
- If a quote stands alone, the last full stop lies inside the quotation mark.
  Example:
  'For relaxation, I like to bake cakes.'

Ideas for further practice

- Place around the classroom large written examples of quotations within quotations with carriers. Highlight all punctuation in contrasting colours.
- Pupils write examples of unpunctuated quotations within quotations, with and without carriers. They swap with a partner who adds the punctuation. Together, they correct and discuss the placement of all punctuation in their examples.

Answers

1. Harry took a book from the shelf labelled 'Natural history'.

   'Hey!' he announced. 'It says here "Mountains provide over half of the world's fresh water requirements". I didn't realise that.'

   'They're known as the "water towers of the world" I believe', answered Lydia.

   Harry replaced the book and picked up a letter which had caught his eye. He handed it to his sister.

   'You should take a look at this.'

   Lydia took the letter.

   'The standard of Lydia's school work', the head teacher had written, 'has fallen dramatically since her involvement in the school's production of "Grease". If she does not "pull her socks up" she will find herself enjoying the performance as a member of the audience rather than as one of the cast'.

2. Teacher check

   > In direct speech, the presence and position of a carrier affects the punctuation of the quotation.
   >
   > The punctuation guidelines followed in this book are those outlined in the *Style manual for authors, editors and printers* (sixth edition) 2002.

Quotation marks
in handwritten work

In handwritten work, *quotation marks* have many uses. Single quotation marks are used to enclose:

- **the quoted work of other authors**
  example: 'The scent of the mountain heather', wrote Aisling, 'reminded me of my childhood days'.

- **colloquial references in formal writing**
  example: He behaved like 'a bear with a sore head' throughout the whole day.

- **terms introduced by a word or phrase such as 'labelled' and 'the expression'**
  example: The expression 'There's nothing worse than' drives me crazy.

If any of these are written within direct speech, *double quotation marks* are used instead.

Example: 'In which Jane Austen novel', asked the teacher, 'does the statement,
"Any savage can dance" appear?'

1. Add the quotation marks to the text.

Harry took a book from the shelf labelled Natural history.

Hey! he announced. It says here, Mountains provide over half of the

world's fresh water requirements. I didn't realise that.

They're known as the water towers of the world I believe, answered Lydia.

Harry replaced the book and picked up a letter which had caught his eye. He handed it to his sister.

You should take a look at this.

Lydia took the letter.

The standard of Lydia's school work, the head teacher had written, has fallen dramatically since her involvement in the school's production of Grease. If she does not pull her socks up she will find herself enjoying the performance as a member of the audience rather than as one of the cast.

2. Write and punctuate a piece of text that includes:

- direct speech with and without carriers
- examples of other uses of quotation marks

Punctuation

Colons and semicolons

Focus

Colons and semicolons

Definitions

- A **colon** is a punctuation mark used to let readers know that information will follow.
- A **semicolon** is a punctuation mark used to let readers know they need to make a longer pause than for a comma.

Explanation

The use of standardised marks in writing such as colons and semicolons clarifies meaning for a reader.

- Examples of when a colon is used include:

  1. Introducing a list of a series of items.

     The following are important environmental issues: global warming, pollution and soil degradation.

     Note: When the list flows naturally as part of the sentence, as when the words 'such as' or 'include' come before a list, a colon is not used.

     Extremely important environmental issues include global warming, pollution and soil degradation.

  2. Introducing an explanation, example or quotation.

     A famous quote in one of Shakespeare's plays reads: 'To be or not to be, that is the question'.

  3. Introducing offset lists.

     Instructions:

     1. Fill the eyedropper with water.

     2. Practise squeezing the water out, one drop at a time.

  4. Introducing each character's dialogue in a playscript.

     Brandon: I refuse to do it!

  5. Introducing the subtitle of a book.

     Antarctica: The frozen continent

- Examples of when a semicolon is used include:

  1. Before words and expressions such as 'however', 'for example' and 'therefore'.

     The resort offered a variety of outdoor activities; for example, scuba diving, mini-golf and tennis.

  2. To separate items in a sentence that contains commas.

     Mum enjoyed reading, walking and mini golf; Dad enjoyed scuba diving, walking and tennis; and we enjoyed mini-golf, swimming in the pool and go-karting.

  3. To join two ideas in a sentence instead of using a conjunction.

     The losing team is coming off the court; some are looking very disappointed.

     Note: Each sentence part could stand alone as a sentence. The word 'and' could have been used to join the sentences. A semicolon is used instead of a full stop for effect and variety.

Worksheet information

- Show pupils examples in familiar books of where colons are used. Discuss how they are used in several ways. The worksheet concentrates on a common way pupils would use them in their writing.

- Show pupils examples in familiar books of where semicolons are used. Again, discuss how they are used in several ways. The worksheet concentrates on two common ways pupils would use them in their writing at this level.

Ideas for further practice

- Pupils identify colons in book titles with subtitles, recipe procedures and science experiments, where colons are used in offset lists, and in playscripts to introduce a new character speaking.

- Find examples of sentences using semicolons in books and create a display of sentence excerpts to discuss and refer to.

Answers

1. (a) These were the chef's recommendations**:** garlic prawns, beef medallions and chocolate mud cake.

   (b) The waiter explained there were several ways to cook the medallions**:** rare, medium or well done and with or without sauce.

   (c) At the end of the meal we told the chef**:** 'Our meals were cooked to perfection'.

2. More money is being invested in space programmes**;** therefore, more discoveries should be made about the universe.

3. Next week, we will study Jupiter, the largest planet**;** Venus, the hottest planet**;** and Saturn, the ringed planet.

Colons and semicolons

COLONS

A *colon* is a punctuation mark used to let readers know that information such as a list, explanation, example or quotation will follow.

For example: The comment on the front of the menu read: 'Many mouth-watering morsels await'.

1. Rewrite each sentence, adding the colon in the correct place.

   (a) These were the chef's recommendations garlic prawns, beef medallions and chocolate mud cake.

   _____

   _____

   (b) The waiter explained there were several ways to cook the medallions rare, medium or well done and with or without sauce.

   _____

   _____

   (c) At the end of the meal we told the chef 'Our meals were cooked to perfection'.

   _____

   _____

SEMICOLONS

A *semicolon* is a punctuation mark used to let readers know they need to take a longer pause than for a comma.

A *semicolon* can be used before words such as 'however', 'for example' and 'therefore'.

For example: Earth is the only planet thought to sustain life; however, Mars may be a possibility.

2. Rewrite this sentence, adding a semicolon in the correct place.

   More money is being invested in space programmes therefore, more discoveries should be made about the universe.

   _____

   _____

Another way a semicolon can be used is to separate items in a sentence that contains commas.

For example: This week we studied Mars, the red planet; Earth, the blue planet; and Mercury, the smallest planet.

3. Rewrite this sentence, changing incorrect commas to semicolons.

   Next week, we will study Jupiter, the largest planet, Venus, the hottest planet, and Saturn, the ringed planet.

   _____

   _____

Punctuation

Hyphens, dashes and ellipses

Focus

Using hyphens, dashes and ellipses

Definitions

- **Hyphens** are short strokes used to join words.
- **Dashes** are longer strokes used to indicate a break in text.
- **Ellipses** are punctuation marks, usually three full stops in a row, used to show that words have been omitted.

Explanation

- Punctuation facilitates the processes of writing and reading.
- Hyphens, dashes and ellipses have specific roles to play in punctuation.
- A **hyphen** is used to:
  - join words
    Example:
    father-in-law, well-known (as an adjective)
  - create compound numbers between *twenty-one* and *ninety-nine*
  - join a prefix to: a base word; e.g. *ex-army*; a capitalised word; *post-Cubism*; a date; e.g. *mid-1600s.*
- Different sources provide slightly different rules for the use of hyphens. For consistency, it is advisable to choose one dictionary for reference and follow its rules.
- A **dash** can be used:
  - to separate a word or group of words within a sentence.
    Example:
    Ocean swimming is exhilarating—if you are a strong swimmer.
  - before a specific list.
    Example:
    I have the key ingredients here—onion, garlic, chilli.
  - in place of parentheses (round brackets).
    Example:
    The regiment—the 5th Division—returned from its tour of duty.

- **Ellipses** are three full stops that are used in writing to show:
  - that a part of a quotation has been omitted (Care must be taken that the omission does not alter the meaning of the quotation.)
  - indecision or incompleteness of speech or thought.
- Question marks, exclamation marks and quotation marks may precede or follow ellipses but other punctuation marks may not.

Worksheet information

- Revise the use of hyphens, dashes and ellipses using examples similar to those on the worksheet.

Ideas for further practice

- Choose a short quotation from a popular, easily accessible book. Decide on a part of the quote to omit. Write the quotation, using ellipses in place of the omission. Give to a partner to find the omitted part of the quote. Discuss whether the omission lost or maintained the sense of the original quotation.
- Research and discuss rules for using hyphens. Choose three compound words which may require a hyphen and check in different dictionaries. Are there any discrepancies?

Answers

1. (b) sixty-three, part-time, son-in-law's, up-to-date, two-year-old, grand-daughter, mid-40s, T-shirt, state-of-the-art, ex-army

2. (a) Skateboarding is great fun—except when you fall off and hurt yourself.
   (b) The activities available—pony trekking, abseiling and canoeing—last for half a day.
   (c) Don't be late for school again—or you will suffer the consequences.
   (d) The science fiction film *Dark star*—1974—is still popular today.

3. 'Breakfast!' thought Sam. 'Toast and ... no, cereal ... or maybe bacon and ... no, just coffee, I think.'

4. (a) '... I have a dream that my four little children ... will not be judged by the colour of their skin but by the content of their character ...'
   (b) '... will one day live in a nation where they ...'

Hyphens, dashes and ellipses

HYPHENS

> *Hyphens* (-) are short strokes used to create some compound words.

1. (a) Read the text. Hyphens have been omitted from ten examples.

> *Mrs Jones, who was sixty three years old, worked part time as an architect in her son in law's firm. She liked to keep up to date with all the latest developments in the business. She was expecting a visit from Robert and her two year old grand daughter.*
>
> *Robert was in his mid 40s. He arrived wearing a T shirt and scruffy jeans. He wanted some help with the plans for a state of the art house he was designing for an ex army friend.*

   (b) Write the ten hyphenated examples.

   _____

   _____

   _____

DASHES

> **Dashes (—) are longer strokes used:**
> - to separate words in a sentence
> - in place of round brackets
> - before a list

2. **Draw a vertical mark to indicate where a dash has been omitted.**

   (a) Skateboarding is great fun except when you fall off and hurt yourself.

   (b) The activities available pony trekking, abseiling and canoeing last for half a day.

   (c) Don't be late for school again or you will suffer the consequences.

   (d) The science fiction film *Dark star* 1974 is still popular today.

ELLIPSES

> **Ellipses (...) are used to show:**
> - that a part of a quotation has been omitted
> - indecision or unfinished speech

3. (a) Read the sentence. Three sets of ellipses have been omitted.

> *'Breakfast!' thought Sam. 'Toast and no, cereal or maybe bacon and no, just coffee, I think.'*

   (b) Write the sentence adding the ellipses.

   _____

   _____

4. **In 1963, Martin Luther King made his famous 'I have a dream' speech.**

> '   *I have a dream that my four little children*   *will not be judged by the colour of their skin but by the content of their character*   '

   (a) Add the three sets of ellipses to the section of the speech in the box.

   (b) Find and write the omitted text using correct punctuation.

Figures of speech
Colloquialisms and jargon

Focus

Colloquialisms and jargon

Definitions

- **Colloquialisms** are correct but informal language.

  Example:

  The expression 'on the blink' is a colloquialism for something that is not working properly.

- **Jargon** is words, phrases or clauses used by people in a particular job or group that can be difficult for others to understand.

  Example:

  'slam dunk', 'timeout' and 'three-point play' are jargon used in a basketball game

Explanation

- Investigating figures of speech such as colloquialisms and jargon develops and enriches pupils' vocabulary and fosters an interest in language.

- Colloquialisms are sometimes also known as 'slang'. Some colloquialisms are recognised worldwide, while others are specific to a country. If colloquialisms are used in formal writing, quotation marks should be used to indicate the colloquial word or phrase.

- Jargon is often referred to as 'technical language'. It makes communication quicker and easier among members of a group who understand it. However, it can be difficult for others not familiar with the jargon to understand, so the needs of the wider audience should be considered.

Worksheet information

- The activities on page 77 could be completed in pairs or a small group where pupils general knowledge could be 'pooled' and they could work together to identify the meanings of the colloquialisms and jargon. Some pupils will be more familiar than others with the use of specific words and phrases.

Ideas for further practice

- Pupils identify colloquialisms used by the teacher, other pupils and in television programmes. Compile a list to display and discuss.

- Brainstorm to list other words and phrases used in sporting jargon by commentators, coaches and players.

Answers

1. The paragraph pupils rewrite should indicate the following:

   I knew today was going to be *a day where things went wrong*. It began when I combed my hair and realised it would be *a day where I wouldn't be able to get my hair to look good*. Then, at *breakfast*, I dropped my toast *buttered side down* on the floor. I nearly *slipped over* when I stepped on it. Later, Mum yelled for me *to hurry up* if I wanted a lift to school. When I got in the car she said I looked *very scruffy*.

2. (a) broken their drought: finally won a game

   (b) all but their die-hard fans had counted them out: everyone except their loyal fans thought they would lose

   (c) hardly been able to buy a goal: hardly scored a goal

   (d) neck and neck: the scores were close

   (e) on fire: playing really well

   (f) all over bar the shouting: it was obvious the Demons were going to win

   (g) hadn't sunk in yet: they couldn't believe they had actually won

Colloquialisms and jargon

A **colloquialism** is an expression used in everyday language but not in formal language.
For example: Dad **slammed on the anchors** to avoid hitting the car.
(The formal words would be 'pushed hard on the brake'.)

1. Read the text below and discuss the meaning of the colloquialisms <u>in bold print</u>. Then rewrite the text using formal language.

> *I knew today was going to be **a disaster looking for a place to happen**. It began when I combed my hair and realised it would be **a bad hair day**. Then, at **brekkie**, I dropped my toast **sunny-side down** on the floor. I nearly came **a cropper** when I stepped on it. Later, Mum yelled for me **to get a wriggle on** if I wanted a lift to school. When I got in the car she said I looked **like something the cat dragged in**.*

_____

_____

_____

_____

_____

_____

_____

Jargon is language used by people in a particular job or group.
For example: a **chronic disease** is medical jargon for a long-term illness or condition.

2. When you listen to or watch a sports broadcast you will hear the commentators using sporting jargon to describe the game. Read the sports report below and explain what each word, phrase or clause in bold print means.

> *At last the Demons have **broken their drought** with a stunning victory over the Lions. **All but their die-hard fans had counted them out** before the game. In previous weeks, the Demons have **hardly been able to buy a goal**. It was **neck and neck** until half time but the Demons were **on fire** in the last half. By three-quarter time it was **all over bar the shouting**. The captain said the win **hadn't sunk in yet** but should when the celebrations began.*

(a) broken their drought _____

(b) all but their die-hard fans had counted them out_____

_____

(c) hardly been able to buy a goal _____

(d) neck and neck _____

(e) on fire _____

(f) all over bar the shouting _____

(g) hadn't sunk in yet _____

Figures of speech
Hyperbole

Focus

Hyperbole

Definition

- **Hyperbole** is an exaggeration or overstatement.

Explanation

- Hyperbole is pronounced hy-per-bol-e, with the emphasis on the second syllable and ending with a long **e** sound.

- Hyperbole is an example of figurative speech that uses exaggeration to emphasise the magnitude of things such as size, feeling, effort or reaction.

  Example:

  > I **nearly died laughing**.
  > I could write better than that **with both hands tied behind my back**.

  Such statements are not meant to be taken literally but they demonstrate the intensity of meaning.

- Hyperbole differs from simile and metaphor in that it is used primarily for emphasis and persuasion rather than for description.

- Hyperbole is an integral part of the spoken English language and an understanding of it is important for the comprehension of some humorous, informal writing.

Worksheet information

- There are many Internet sites on which examples of hyperbole can be found. Give pupils the opportunity to compile lists and then discuss their use and meaning.

- Explain that hyperbole is generally regarded as using exaggeration to make a point. It is often humorous and, in some cases, the more 'over the top' the better.

- Give starter phrases for the pupils to add an example of hyperbole:

  Example:

  > The heat was so intense …
  > The fruit was so bitter …
  > The teacher was so unpopular …
  > The house was so dilapidated …

- Read through the poem and discuss the examples of hyperbole and their meaning.

- In part (c) of Question 1, pupils use plain language to describe the winter day. Adjectives are required but only to convey the message, not to make the text interesting.

- Pupils work independently for the first part of Question 2, writing examples of hyperbole for both types of description. They may need to continue on a separate sheet of paper.

- Joining forces with a partner, one pupil compiles the examples for the 'should be chosen' description, the other, for the 'should not be chosen'. Pupils use the examples in a description which can then be read to the class.

Ideas for further practice

- Use hyperbole to write a poem on a chosen subject. Collect and redistribute poems among the class to be illustrated. Display poems and illustrations on the same wall but mixed up. Study poems and illustrations to determine which belongs with which.

- Sitting in a circle, one pupil says a starter phrase: e.g. 'I was so tired …' and then throws a beanbag to another pupil who must finish the sentence using an example of hyperbole. That pupil then gives another starter phrase before throwing the beanbag to someone else to continue.

Answers

1. (b) The blood in my veins began to freeze, I rose three metres above the ground, The rain pierced my skin

   (c) Teacher check. Possible answer: The day was extremely cold with very strong winds and heavy, piercing rain.

2. Teacher check

Hyperbole

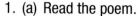

Hyperbole is a figure of speech often using exaggeration and humour to emphasise meaning. It is not meant to be taken literally.

For example: The lake was so deep it extended to the Earth's core.
The house was so untidy that even rampaging burglars refused to enter.

1. (a) Read the poem.

(b) Underline the examples of hyperbole in the text.

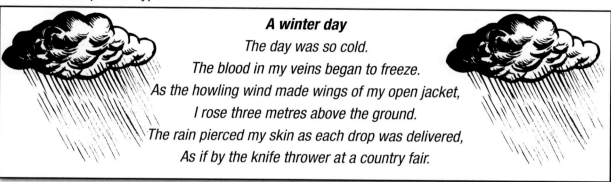

A winter day

The day was so cold.
The blood in my veins began to freeze.
As the howling wind made wings of my open jacket,
I rose three metres above the ground.
The rain pierced my skin as each drop was delivered,
As if by the knife thrower at a country fair.

(c) Translate the poem into a piece of simple narrative using appropriate adjectives to convey the message.

2. (a) Write examples of hyperbole that could be used to convince a sports coach why a friend **should** or **should not** be chosen for a first team.

Should be chosen	Should not be chosen
e.g. She can kick the ball so accurately, she can hit the centre of a dartboard from 100 metres.	e.g. He kicks so badly even his own team dives for cover.

(b) Add your hyperbole to those written by a partner about the same person and write a final description of why your friend should be chosen for the team.

(c) Read your description to the class.

Figures of speech

Idioms

IDIOMS

Focus

Idioms

Definition

- An **idiom** is a saying peculiar to a language in which real and literal meanings are different.

Explanation

- Idioms are metaphorical phrases that are not meant to be taken literally. The true meaning of an idiom cannot be found from the meaning of its individual words but is learned through its use in context.

- Idioms are an integral part of the English language and an understanding of them is essential for the comprehension of a wide range of texts and for interesting writing.

Worksheet information

- Before completing the worksheet, discuss idioms and their role in adding to the richness of the English language. What idioms are the pupils familiar with? Do they know the origins of any idioms? Why do they think idioms have survived over generations? Do they think idioms are a valuable part of the language? Why/Why not?

- Ask pupils to close their eyes as you read a sentence containing an idiom. Ask them how they visualised the idiom. What do they think it means? How well do they think it conveys its meaning?

- In pairs, pupils discuss the text and identify the six idioms. They discuss and record the idioms and their meanings.

- In Question 2, pupils illustrate and label two idioms which they often use or hear. Before labelling the illustrations, they could ask other class members if they recognise the idioms they represent.

- In Question 3, pupils research different idioms before choosing one which appeals to them. Considering its meaning, pupils create another expression with the same meaning.

Ideas for further practice

- Create an illustrated display of idioms, their meanings and origins.
- Create an illustrated class book of idioms in context.

Answers

1. (a) up to their ears – very busy

   (b) tail end – the last part of a job/situation

   (c) dead on their feet – extremely tired

   (d) angel of mercy – someone who arrives just as he/she is needed

   (e) sleep the sleep of the dead – sleep soundly

2.–3. Teacher check

Idioms

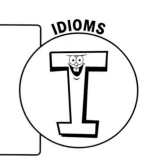

An *idiom* is a phrase whose meaning is not related to its individual words:

For example: To 'face the music' is to confront and take responsibility for one's actions

'sitting pretty' is to be in a fortunate situation

'plain sailing' is progressing without problems.

Kevin and Luis were up to their ears in paper. They were at the tail end of a school project which had to be delivered the next morning. As usual, they had been slow beginning the assignment and now they were dead on their feet trying to complete it on time. Like an angel of mercy, Kevin's mum came in with supper just as they were filing the last sheets of paper.

Each boy knew he would sleep the sleep of the dead after such a mammoth effort.

---

1. Underline the five idioms in the text. Work with a partner to find and write the idioms and their meanings.

   (a) _____   _____

   (b) _____   _____

   (c) _____   _____

   (d) _____   _____

   (e) _____   _____

2. Illustrate and label two idioms that you often use.

3. (a) Research to find an idiom that appeals to you. Write the idiom and its meaning.

   _____

   _____

   (b) Create two new idioms that have the same meaning as your chosen one.

   (c) Do you think either of these idioms will catch on?   (yes)   (no)

Figures of speech

Similes and metaphors

Focus

Similes and metaphors

Definitions

- A **simile** compares one thing with another. Similes are usually introduced by the words 'as' or 'like'.

  Example:

  'He was as cunning as a fox.'
  'She slept like a log.'

- A **metaphor** is a comparison between two things without the use of 'as' or 'like'. Metaphors say something *is* something else.

  Example:

  'The sunset was a rainbow of colours.'
  'A blanket of snow covered the street.'

Explanation

- Similes and metaphors are figures of speech. They are examples of figurative language, as opposed to literal language (stating a fact). In figurative language, words are used to create mental images by comparing ideas. These comparisons help the reader to more clearly imagine the person, place or thing being described.

- Writers use similes to emphasise a certain characteristic. They make writing more interesting, entertaining and colourful, as they often forge a link between two unlike subjects.

  Example:

  *The **children** ran around the playground <u>like</u> **a pack of wild animals**.*

- Like similes, metaphors compare and link two subjects that are not usually linked. However, while a simile is a simple comparison, a metaphor states that two subjects are the same. Metaphors give one object the attributes of the other.

  Example:

  In the playground, the children <u>were</u> a pack of wild animals.

  The children have been given the attributes of a 'pack of wild animals', being 'loud' and 'untamed'.

- Metaphors are considered stronger than similes.

Worksheet information

- Read the definitions of metaphors and similes at the top of the page with the class. Ask the pupils for further examples of each.

- Read the poem with the class. Pupils can work in pairs or small groups to identify the metaphors and similes in the poem.

- Work through Question 2 with the class. Pupils categorise the statements as metaphors or similes in Question 3. In Question 4, pupils explain the metaphor. Ask the class to consider the function of a key (to open doors). Pupils write their own similes in Question 5. When complete, ask for volunteers to share their writing with the class.

Ideas for further practice

- With adult supervision, use the Internet to view popular song lyrics to find examples of similes and metaphors. Work in small groups to write explanations for each.

- As a class, read the classical narrative poem *The Lady of Shalott* by Alfred Lord Tennyson. Identify and discuss the similes and metaphors found in the poem.

- Write a poem containing metaphors or similes, comparing your family to an object of your choice (such as a table, a first-aid box etc.).

Answers

1. Note: Underlined text = simile   Bold text = metaphor
   To those who hurriedly pass him by
   He is a shadow, a pile of old rags
   His face is weathered <u>like a forgotten apple</u>
   He's <u>as useless as torn shopping bags</u>
   Camouflaged in dirt <u>like a soldier</u>
   He's a rat in the gutters and streets
   He shuffles from one bin to another
   <u>Like a hungry child</u>, he swiftly eats

2. (a) the homeless man; a rat
   (b) He scurries and scavenges like a rat.
   (c) It is not a simile because it does not contain 'as' or 'like'.
   (d) He's like a rat in the gutters and streets.

3. (a) Metaphor   (b) Simile
   (c) Simile   (d) Simile
   (e) Metaphor   (f) Metaphor

4. Suggested answer: As keys open doors, the metaphor means that obtaining an education will open doors to a good job.

5. Teacher check

Similes and metaphors

A simile compares one thing with another using the words *as* or *like*. For example: *'as white as snow'*, *'like peas in a pod'*	A metaphor is also a comparison. It says one thing *is* something else. For example: *'Her eyes were diamonds.'*

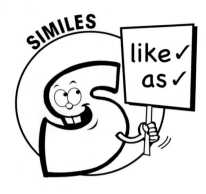

Forgotten

To those who hurriedly pass him by
He is a shadow, a pile of old rags
His face is weathered like a forgotten apple
He's as useless as torn shopping bags
Camouflaged in dirt like a soldier
He's a rat in the gutters and streets
He shuffles from one bin to another
Like a hungry child, he swiftly eats

1. Read the poem. Underline the four similes in red. Underline the three metaphors in blue.

2. 'He's a rat in the gutters and streets.'

    (a) Which things are being compared?

    _____

    (b) Explain the literal meaning of the metaphor. (What the author is trying to say?)

    _____

    _____

    (c) Why is it a metaphor and not a simile?

    _____

    (d) Rewrite the line as a simile.

    _____

    _____

3. Read the statements and write **S** for simile or **M** for metaphor in the box.

    (a) My memory is a cold foggy night. ◯   (b)   The steak was as tough as old leather. ◯

    (c) The bride was as radiant as a rose. ◯   (d)   The stars are like pinpricks in the sky. ◯

    (e) He was a giant striding across the land. ◯   (f)   His face was an old weathered map. ◯

4. Explain the metaphor: *'Education is the key to a good job'.*

    _____

    _____

5. (a) On the back of this sheet, write at least five similes related to the beach (the waves, the sand, the sun etc.).

    (b) Rewrite the similes as metaphors.

    (c) Combine the similes and metaphors to create a beach-themed poem.

Figures of speech

Proverbs

Focus

Proverbs

Definition

- A **proverb** is a wise, usually short saying that has been used for a long time.

    Example:

    Beauty is in the eye of the beholder.

Explanation

- Proverbs are short memorable sayings that express a truth, warning, practical idea or useful thought. Most proverbs aim to teach something. Not as many proverbs are used today as previously. The literal meaning of many proverbs may differ from their accepted meaning. The origins and meanings of many proverbs are often hard to track. Many have changed from their original forms.

- An apt definition for a proverb is 'a short sentence based on long experience'.

- The study of proverbs is called 'paremiology' and a collection of proverbs is called a 'paremiography'.

- Internet sites provide valuable references for access to French, English, Chinese, Arabic and African proverbs.

- Proverbs can contain a variety of literacy features including alliteration, rhyme, hyperbole, paradox and personification.

    Example:

    *'Birds of a feather flock together' (alliteration),
    'A stitch in time saves nine' (alliteration and rhyme),
    'An Englishman's home is his castle' and 'It never rains but it pours' (hyperbole),
    'Failure teaches success' and 'Familiarity breeds contempt' (paradox)
    and 'Walls have ears' (personification)*

Worksheet information

- Pupils should complete Questions 1 to 2. Discuss the definition in Question 3.

- The proverbs in Question 4 are very familiar. However, assistance and collaboration may be necessary.

- Pupils can complete Question 5 independently.

Ideas for further practice

- Find proverbs which illustrate specific literacy features such as alliteration, personification and rhyme.

- Research, read and discuss proverbs from different cultures.

- Find proverbs which can be applied to real-life problems which arise in the classroom, playground or school.

    Example:

    'Honesty is the best policy', 'If you want a friend, be a friend', 'Honey catches more flies than vinegar', 'Actions speak louder than words', 'All things are difficult before they are easy'

- Ask the pupils to write a fable to illustrate a particular proverb.

Answers

1.–3. Teacher check

4. (a) A stitch in time saves nine.
   (b) All that glitters is not gold.
   (c) Beauty is only skin deep.
   (d) All work and no play makes Jack a dull boy.
   (e) An apple a day keeps the doctor away.
   (f) Empty vessels make the most noise.
   (g) Fingers were made before forks.
   (h) You are what you eat.
   (i) Two wrongs don't make a right.
   (j) Home is where the heart is.

5. Answers will vary but should be similar to:
   (a) People will tell bad news very quickly.
   (b) Be grateful for what you have, even if it is not as much as you want.
   (c) A foolish person spends his/her money very quickly.
   (d) Don't judge people by their appearance only. What's inside is more important.

Proverbs

1. Read the proverbs below.

- Actions speak louder than words.
- Necessity is the mother of invention.
- Every cloud has a silver lining.
- Cheats never prosper.
- All's well that ends well.
- Blood is thicker than water.

2. With a partner discuss what the proverbs mean, then complete the definition.

A proverb is _____

_____.

3. Compare your definition to the one below.

A proverb is a wise, usually short saying that has been used for a long time. Proverbs usually express a basic truth, an idea or try to teach something.

PROVERBS

4. Write the endings for these well-known proverbs.

(a) A stitch in time _____.

(b) All that glitters _____.

(c) Beauty is only _____.

(d) All work and no play makes _____.

(e) An apple a day _____.

(f) Empty vessels _____.

(g) Fingers were made _____.

(h) You are what _____.

(i) Two wrongs don't _____.

(j) Home is where _____.

5. What is each proverb trying to teach?

(a) Bad news travels fast.

_____

_____

_____

(b) Half a loaf is better than none.

_____

_____

_____

(c) A fool and his money are soon parted.

_____

_____

_____

(d) Don't judge a book by is cover.

_____

_____

_____